SO-CBB-247

SRA

Skills Practice
Workbook

**Level 4
Book 1**

McGraw Hill **SRA**

Columbus, OH

SRAonline.com

Send all inquiries to this address:
SRA/McGraw-Hill
4400 Easton Commons
Columbus, OH 43219-6188

ISBN: 978-0-07-619475-9
MHID: 0-07-619475-2

2 3 4 5 6 7 8 9 QPD 13 12 11 10 09

The **McGraw·Hill** Companies

Table of Contents

Unit 1 — Risks and Consequences

Unit 2 Nature's Delicate Balance

③ Unit 3 A Changing State

Name _____ **Date** _____

Suffix *-ous*

 **Focus**
- A **suffix** is an addition to the end of a word.
- A **root word** or **base word** is a word to which a suffix can be added.
- The suffix *-ous* means "full of" or "characterized by."
- Adding the suffix *-ous* to the word *danger* makes the word *dangerous*, or "full of danger."
- If the base word ends in a consonant + *y*, change the *y* to *i* before adding the suffix *-ous*

 **Practice** Add *-ous* to each base word below to create a new word.

1. hazard _____

2. envy _____

3. glory _____

4. victory _____

5. continue _____

6. fame _____

7. study _____

8. harmony _____

9. joy _____

10. adventure _____

 **Apply** Look up the meaning for each of the words in the following box. Then add the words to the appropriate sentences.

various	vigorous	marvelous	jealous	delicious

11. Jasmine had a _____ assortment of stuffed animals in her room.

12. Mr. Jackson made a _____ appetizer for the potluck.

13. The instructions on the bottle read to mix well before opening, so I gave

it a _____ shake.

14. My brother was so _____ at the Shakespeare play last night that he got a standing ovation.

15. Even though Marc's bike is bigger than Sherry's, she is not

_____ of him.

Circle all the words that have the suffix -ous in the sentences below.

16. I though that Mike was very courageous to write the senator; I would have been nervous.

17. Pauline was explaining her family's camping trip and mentioned how mysterious the woods are at night.

18. The comic's outrageous stand-up routine was memorable.

19. I was afraid that I looked ridiculous with my new haircut, but Tanya told me that I looked great.

20. The new school seemed monstrous until our teacher took us on a tour.

Selection Vocabulary

headland (hĕd' lənd) *n.* a point of high land that sticks out into the water; a cape (page 18)

companions (kəm pan' yənz) *n.* plural of **companion:** a person who often goes along with another; a friend; a comrade (page 21)

pursued (pûr sōōd') *v.* past tense of **pursue:** to chase (page 21)

tides (tīdz) *n.* plural of **tide:** the rise and fall of the sea (page 23)

sandspit (sand' spit') *n.* a narrow point of sand extending into a body of water (page 23)

lessened (les' ənd) *v.* past tense of **lessen:** to make or become less (page 23)

bow (bou) *n.* the front part of a ship (page 26)

seeping (sēp' ing) *v.* form of **seep:** to flow or spread slowly (page 26)

lacking (lak' ing) *v.* form of **lack:** to be without (page 26)

fiber (fī' bər) *n.* a piece of cloth (page 26)

idly (īd' lē) *adv.* not doing anything (page 28)

dozed (dōzd) *v.* past tense of **doze:** to sleep lightly (page 31)

 **Circle the word in parentheses that best fits each sentence.**

1. The lazy dog slept (lacking / idly) on the couch.

2. The bank robber was being (dozed / pursued) by the police officer.

3. The milk was (lessened / seeping) from the carton.

4. The (companions / tides) walked across the beach looking for shells.

5. When the weather turned cold, Sarah used the (fiber / tides) as a blanket.

6. The cat yawned and (pursued / dozed) in the afternoon sun.

7. I would run the race, but I am (lacking / cover) good running shoes.

8. The (deserted / tides) are strong on the shore of this island.

**Apply** **Match each word on the left to its definition on the right.**

9. fiber   **a.** being without

10. tides   **b.** chased

11. lacking   **c.** rise and fall of the sea

12. idly   **d.** friends or comrades

13. pursued   **e.** not doing anything

14. companions   **f.** slept lightly

15. headland   **g.** piece of cloth

16. dozed   **h.** a high point of land that sticks out into the water

Write two sentences using at least one of the vocabulary words from this lesson in each.

17. _____

_____

_____

18. _____

_____

_____

Author's Point of View

Focus Writers must decide the point of view from which a story is told. All stories are told through a narrator—the person who tells the story. The narrator can tell the story from

- the **third-person point of view.** The narrator is an outside observer and uses pronouns such as *he, she,* and *they* when telling the story.

- the **first-person point of view.** The narrator is a character in the story and uses pronouns such as *I, me,* and *my* when telling the story.

Practice **Look through "Island of the Blue Dolphins." Find three sentences that show the author's point of view. Write the page number, the sentence, and the point of view in the spaces below.**

1. Page: _____ Point of view: _____

Sentence: _____

_____

2. Page: _____ Point of view: _____

Sentence: _____

_____

3. Page: _____ Point of view: _____

Sentence: _____

_____

Read the following passage. Answer the questions about the author's point of view.

My mom and I planted a flower garden in the vacant lot at the end of the block. We knew it was a risky project because dogs or pranksters might dig up the flowers. But to my mom and me, the risk was worth taking. The colorful flowers added beauty to our neighborhood.

4. What is the author's point of view? _____

5. What words tell you the author's point of view?

_____

Apply **Rewrite the above passage using the third-person point of view.**

_____

_____

_____

_____

_____

_____

_____

_____

Generating Questions to Investigate

What other questions about risks and consequences would you like to learn more about? Write them here.

_____

_____

_____

_____

Now think about these questions. Are there people whom you admire because they take risks? Who are they? What risks have they taken?

Person   **Risk**

_____   _____

_____   _____

_____   _____

_____   _____

Below are more questions to think about:

• Does everyone agree on what a risk is?

• Do you have to be a certain kind of person to take risks?

• Can you do things to make a risk less risky?

Think of ways in which you could find answers to these questions. Write them here.

_____

_____

Choosing Appropriate Sources

Make a list of topics that you want to learn more about from "Island of the Blue Dolphins." Some possible topics to investigate include the author of the story or the ways dolphins communicate.

Think of topics you would like to learn more about. Write three topics here.

_____

_____

Choose the topic you would most like to learn about.

_____

There are many sources you can use to investigate your favorite topic.

Encyclopedia   Newspapers   Interviews
Book   Dictionary   DVDs and videotapes
Magazines   Internet   Pamphlets and brochures

Choose two sources you could use to investigate your topic.

_____

What type of information do these sources contain?

_____

_____

What might you learn from these sources about your topic?

_____

_____

Writing: Describing a Setting

Location: Where will your story take place?

_____

Time: When will your story occur?

_____

The setting of a story is almost like another character in the story. You need to describe your setting, both location and time, very well so your audience will be able to visualize the background of the story.

Think of the setting descriptions in "Island of the Blue Dolphins" or another fictional story you have read recently. Are you able to close your eyes and visualize the setting if someone else reads it to you? Place yourself into the story, and provide words that answer the questions to use in your story.

What do you see? _____

_____

What do you smell? _____

_____

What do you hear? _____

_____

What do you feel? _____

_____

What is the landscape like? _____

_____

Revising

Use this checklist to revise your setting description.

- ☐ Is your setting believable?
- ☐ Did you go back and add details where they were needed?
- ☐ Have you used descriptive words?
- ☐ Is this historically accurate?

Editing

Use this checklist to correct mistakes. Use proofreader's marks as you read your first draft.

- ☐ Make sure that all words are spelled correctly.
- ☐ Check all punctuation to make sure that it is correct.
- ☐ Make sure that sentences and proper nouns begin with capital letters.

Publishing

Use this checklist to get ready for publication.

- ☐ Write or type a neat final copy.
- ☐ Read your work one more time. Correct any errors.

Comparatives and Base-Word Families

Focus

- **Comparatives** are words that are used to compare two things.
- You can form a comparative by adding **-er** to base words.
- Adding -er may require changes to the base word.
- Sometimes the y at the end of an adjective or adverb changes to i before adding -er.
- Some words are related because they have the same **base word.**
- When you know the meaning of a base word, you can begin to determine the meaning of the other words in the base-word family.

Practice

Remove the -er from each of the following words and write the base word.

1. greater _____

2. closer _____

3. nearer _____

4. bigger _____

5. happier _____

6. neater _____

7. lighter _____

8. colder _____

9. slower _____

10. gentler _____

11. taller _____

12. younger _____

Word List

1. basement
2. basic
3. basically
4. bigger
5. closer
6. colder
7. gentler
8. greater
9. happier
10. hotter
11. lighter
12. lovely
13. lovingly
14. nearer
15. neater
16. older
17. quicker
18. slower
19. taller
20. younger

Challenge Words

21. baseline
22. farther
23. loveable

Write all of the spelling words that contain the base word *base*.

13. _____

14. _____

15. _____

16. _____

Write all of the spelling words that contain the base word *love*.

17. _____

18. _____

19. _____

Apply Use the following spelling words to write a sentence that compares two things.

20. gentler _____

_____

21. farther _____

_____

22. hotter _____

_____

23. colder _____

_____

24. quicker _____

_____

Nouns

 **Focus**   **Nouns** are words that name people, places, things, or ideas.

Rule	Example
• A **common noun** names *any* person, place, thing, or idea.	• student, school, chalkboard
• A **proper noun** names particular persons, places, things, or ideas. They always begin with capital letters.	• New York, June, Thursday
• A **concrete noun** names something we can touch or see.	• dolphin, girl, water
• An **abstract noun** names something we cannot touch or see, such as an idea or emotion.	• friendship, honesty, happiness

 **Practice**   **Read this paragraph. Look at the words in bold type. Underline the words in bold type that are *concrete* nouns. Circle the words in bold type that are *abstract* nouns.**

Robert heard **laughter** as he walked into the **kitchen.** His mother and

brother were baking granola. The **smell** coming from the **oven** was wonderful.

Robert's **stomach** growled as he waited for the **granola** to be done. It was

hard to have **patience!** Robert remembered the granola his **grandmother** used

to make. The **aroma** was now almost too much for him to take. It filled the

entire **house** with the **smell** of **nuts** and **honey**. When the granola was finally

ready, Robert showed his **happiness** by eating three **bars!**

Apply Look at one of the drawings from "Island of the Blue Dolphins" or another book you have recently read. Briefly describe the drawing or picture. Then list all the concrete, abstract, and proper nouns you observe.

_____

_____

Concrete	Abstract	Proper
_____	_____	_____
_____	_____	_____
_____	_____	_____
_____	_____	_____
_____	_____	_____
_____	_____	_____
_____	_____	_____
_____	_____	_____
_____	_____	_____
_____	_____	_____
_____	_____	_____
_____	_____	_____
_____	_____	_____
_____	_____	_____
_____	_____	_____

Name _____ Date _____

Suffixes *-ly* and *-ist*

 Focus

- Remember that a suffix is an addition to the end of a root or base word.

- Adding the suffix *-ly* to the end of words changes adjectives to adverbs. Adverbs describe verbs, adjectives, or other adverbs.

- If the word ends in *y,* the *y* is changed to *i* before adding *-ly.*

- The suffix *-ist* means "one who practices." In this case, the part of speech of the base word does not change.

- If the word ends with a silent *e,* drop the e before adding the suffix *-ist.*

Practice **Add the suffix *-ly* or *-ist* to make a new word.**

1. loud   _____

2. clear   _____

3. organ   _____

4. soft   _____

5. motor   _____

6. extreme   _____

7. quiet   _____

8. final   _____

9. constant   _____

10. noisy   _____

Apply Add the suffix *-ly* to each root word. Then use each new word in a sentence.

11. complete _____

_____

_____

_____

12. cautious _____

_____

_____

_____

13. proud _____

_____

_____

_____

Add the suffix *-ist* to each root word. Then use each new word in a sentence.

14. bicycle _____

_____

_____

_____

15. archive _____

_____

_____

_____

16. journal _____

_____

Selection Vocabulary

Focus

ownership (ōn' ər ship) *n.* the state or fact of being an owner (page 43)

hastened (hā' sənd) *v.* past tense of **hasten:** to hurry (page 43)

shuddered (shu' dûrd) *v.* past tense of **shudder:** to shake with horror (page 43)

despairing (di spâr' ing) *adj.* form of **despair:** without hope (page 44)

sympathetic (sim' pə the' tik) *adj.* understanding; having a kind feeling for someone (page 44)

delivered (di li' vərd) *v.* past tense of **deliver:** to save from danger (page 45)

agitated (aj' i tā tid') *v.* past tense of **agitate:** to stir up or shake (page 46)

escorted (es kor' təd) *v.* past tense of **escort:** to go along with; to accompany (page 46)

hurdle (hûr' dəl) *n.* a barrier to be jumped over in a race; a difficulty or problem (page 47)

preyed (prād) *v.* past tense of **prey:** to take advantage of; to cause harm to (page 49)

flickering (fli' kûr ing) *adj.* form of **flicker:** to become brighter and then darker over and over (page 53)

concealed (kən sēld') *v.* past tense of **conceal:** to hide (page 55)

Review the vocabulary words and definitions from "Two Tickets to Freedom." Write four sentences that each use at least one of the vocabulary words.

1. _____

_____

2. _____

_____

3. _____

_____

4. _____

_____

 **Write _T_ in the blank if the sentence for the vocabulary word is correct. Write _F_ if the sentence is false. For each _F_ answer, write the word that fits the definition.**

5. _Flickering_ is an adjective meaning "without hope."

_____   _____

6. If something is _delivered,_ it is hidden.

_____   _____

7. A person who is _sympathetic_ is understanding.

_____   _____

8. _Preyed_ means "took advantage of."

_____   _____

9. _Shuddered_ means "hurried."

_____   _____

10. A _flickering_ light becomes brighter and then darker over and over.

_____   _____

11. If someone is saved from danger, that person is _delivered._

_____   _____

12. If someone _hastened,_ he shook with horror.

_____   _____

Framing Questions to Find Information

"Two Tickets to Freedom" includes topics such as slavery and railroads. Based on the story, fill in the chart with questions about five topics you would like to investigate. Write one question for each topic. Then find answers to your questions either by rereading the selection or by investigating the information in another source.

Questions About a Topic	Information I Found
1.	
2.	

Questions About a Topic	Information I Found
3.	
4.	
5.	

Writing: Describing Character

Think Think of Ellen and William Craft, or other characters in a book you have recently read. Even though you have never talked with them, you know their personalities and some of their history. Think about this as you create your characters.

Audience: Who will be your audience for these characters?

_____

Purpose: What are the reasons these characters struggle?

_____

Prewriting Use this character web to organize the traits of your main character. Write the character's name in the middle. Then write one of the character's traits on each of the longer lines. Finally, list behaviors that demonstrate each trait on the shorter lines. Make sure you include personality traits, physical descriptions, sample dialogue, and actions that your character might take.

_____   _____

_____   _____

Character's name

_____   _____

_____   _____

Revising

Use this checklist to revise your character sketch.

☐ Does your character seem like a real person?

☐ Will your reader be able to visualize the character based on your description?

☐ Do you use precise nouns, verbs, adjectives, and adverbs to bring your character to life?

☐ Do your character's traits and motivations match his or her actions?

Editing

Use this checklist to correct mistakes. Use proofreader's marks as you read your first draft.

☐ Make sure that all words are spelled correctly.

☐ Check all punctuation to make sure that it is correct.

☐ Make sure that sentences and proper nouns begin with capital letters.

Publishing

Use this checklist to get ready for publication.

☐ Write or type a neat final copy.

☐ Include a photo or drawing of your character.

☐ Share your character sketch with others. You and your classmates can collect your character sketches together. Discuss how these characters could occupy the same world or interact with one another.

☐ Work with your teacher to create a fictional environment (play, novel, TV show) where these characters could exist, side by side.

Suffix *-ly* and Prefix *dis-*

**Focus**

- Understanding and identifying suffixes and prefixes can help you determine the meaning and spelling of a difficult or unfamiliar word.

- The **suffix -*ly*** means "like or resembling." This suffix will usually change adjectives into adverbs.

- The **prefix *dis-*** means "not or not having." This prefix will not affect the base word's part of speech.

Practice   Sort the following spelling words under the correct heading.

bravely	clearly	dishonest	patiently	directly
eagerly	contently	disrespect	quietly	displace

Suffix -*ly*

1. _____
2. _____
3. _____
4. _____
5. _____
6. _____
7. _____

Prefix *dis-*

8. _____
9. _____
10. _____

Word List

1. bravely
2. cheaply
3. clearly
4. closely
5. constantly
6. contently
7. directly
8. dishonest
9. disinfect
10. displace
11. disrespect
12. finally
13. joyfully
14. loudly
15. patiently
16. proudly
17. quietly
18. really
19. safely
20. softly

Challenge Words

21. discontent
22. dismay
23. eagerly

On the line, write the spelling word that results when the suffix -ly is added to the following base words.

11. real   _____

12. loud   _____

13. cheap   _____

14. joyful   _____

15. safe   _____

Apply   **Circle the words that are spelled correctly.**

16. proudlly   proudly

17. dismay   dismey

18. finally   finalely

19. dissinfect   disinfect

20. discontent   discontinent

21. softely   softly

22. closly   closely

23. constantely   constantly

24. eagerly   eegerly

25. displase   displace

26. realley   really

Name _____ **Date** _____

Plural and Irregular Nouns

 **Focus**

- To make most nouns plural, just add -s at the end of the word.
  Example: planet   planet**s**
- For singular nouns that end in a **consonant** and a *y*, change the *y* to -*i* and add -*es*.
  Example: famil**y**   famil**ies**
- For singular nouns that end in *ch, s, ss,* or *x*, add -*es*.
  Example: lun**ch**   lunch**es**
  Example: cla**ss**   cla**sses**
  Example: bo**x**   box**es**
- For singular nouns ending in *f,* change the *f* to *v* and add -*es*.
  Example: shelf   shel**ves**
- For some singular nouns, there are no rules. You just have to **remember** the plural.
  Example: mouse   **mice**

 **Practice**   **Fill in the plural for each word.**

Singular   **Plural**

1. fox   _____

2. deer   _____

3. turkey   _____

4. puppy   _____

5. lion   _____

6. tiger   _____

7. fly   _____

8. wolf   _____

9. whale   _____

10. goose   _____

Singular	**Plural**
11. _____	dresses
12. _____	moose
13. avenue	_____
14. _____	pennies
15. _____	leaves
16. city	_____
17. building	_____
18. _____	buses
19. _____	teeth
20. dollar	_____
21. _____	mosses
22. dish	_____
23. glass	_____
24. _____	benches
25. _____	houses
26. essay	_____

Circle the correct nouns in the following paragraph.

Jacque loved hiking, but her (boot, boots) no longer fit her. She asked her mom whether she could use her (allowance, allowances) to purchase them. Her mother agreed that Jacque would have to help buy her hiking (supply, supplies), such as (sock, socks), sun-block, and (canteen, canteens). Jacque decided that she should start doing more (chore, chores) to earn more money.

Prefixes *im-* and *un-*

- A **prefix** is an addition to the beginning of a word. (*un*true)
- The prefixes *im-* and *un-* have a similar meaning: "not" or "opposite."

Add the correct prefix (*im-* or *un-*) to each word to give it the opposite meaning. You may use a dictionary if necessary.

1. mature _____

2. steady _____

3. fold _____

4. attached _____

5. familiar _____

6. pure _____

7. cover _____

8. tie _____

 **Apply** Match each definition below with a word from the word box.

impartial	unfit	unskilled	unpopular
impolite	unprepared	unnatural	

9. not well-liked _____

10. not normal _____

11. not good at something _____

12. not ready _____

13. not choosing sides _____

14. not very nice _____

15. not qualified _____

Write a definition for each new word based on the meaning of the prefix and the base word. You may not use the base word in your definition.

16. untidy _____

17. impossible _____

18. unseen _____

19. unhappy _____

20. unequal _____

Selection Vocabulary

Focus

route (rōōt) *n.* a path or road (page 65)

merriment (mâr' i mənt) *n.* fun (page 66)

fluttered (flut' ərd) *v.* past tense of **flutter:** to move or to fly with quick, light, flapping movements (page 67)

silvery (sil' vər' ē) *adj.* resembling silver; of a lustrous grayish-white color (page 69)

tangled (tang' gəld) *v.* past tense of **tangle:** to wrap in a mess (page 69)

miserable (miz' ûr bəl) *adj.* very unhappy (page 69)

obviously (ob' vē əs lē) *adv.* in a way that is easy to see (page 70)

recalled (ri käld') *v.* past tense of **recall:** to remember (page 70)

authoritative (ə thôr' i tā' tiv) *adj.* worthy of belief; reliable (page 71)

cover (ku' vûr) *n.* something that would be good to hide behind (page 73)

surge (sûrj) *n.* a sudden jerk or strain (page 74)

circumstances (sûr' kəm stants' əz) *n.* plural of **circumstance:** the way things are at the moment (page 74)

Practice   **Fill in the blank with a vocabulary word from this lesson to complete each sentence.**

1. The boys _____ the cords when they put away the tools.

2. Grandfather used a plastic _____ to protect the fishing boat.

3. There was _____ at the party.

4. Anne was _____ after she broke her leg.

5. What is the shortest _____ to the river?

6. The smiling father was _____ proud of his son's talents.

7. Carlos laughed as he _____ the first time he tried to ride a bike.

8. Under the _____ Kellie did the best with what she had.

Apply Write the word from the word box that matches each description below.

cover	miserable	obviously	surge
merriment	tangled	circumstances	recalled

9. _____ wrapped in a mess

10. _____ a good place to stay out of view

11. _____ fun

12. _____ easily seen

13. _____ remembered

14. _____ a sudden jerk or strain

15. _____ very unhappy

16. _____ the state of things at the moment

Write two sentences using at least one of the vocabulary words from this lesson in each.

17. _____

_____

_____

18. _____

_____

Cause and Effect

Focus

Cause-and-effect relationships help readers understand why events happen in a certain way.

- A **cause** is why something happens.
- The **effect** is what happens as a result.
- Writers use signal words and phrases to identify cause-and-effect relationships. These words, which include *because, so, if, then, thus, since, for,* and *therefore,* help readers know what happens and why it happens.

Identify

Look through "Mrs. Frisby and the Crow" for examples of cause-and-effect relationships. For each example, write the event that is the cause and the event that is the effect.

1. Cause: _____

_____

Effect: _____

_____

2. Cause: _____

_____

Effect: _____

_____

Practice

Rewrite each pair of sentences as one sentence showing the cause-and-effect relationship.

3. I could not eat dinner. I ate all the apples.

_____

_____

4. Scruffy bit me. I've been afraid of dogs.

_____

_____

5. I could not find my shoes. I was late.

_____

_____

6. Rachel and Jose put in too much sugar. The recipe did not work.

_____

_____

7. It rained for three days. The streets in my town flooded.

_____

_____

8. The space shuttle did not launch. The winds were too high.

_____

_____

Apply **Think about a machine you see every day. Write down how you think it works, using cause-and-effect signal words.**

_____

_____

_____

_____

Comprehension Skill • *Skills Practice 1*

Taking Notes

Focus Taking notes means writing down information from investigation sources. Good notes contain key phrases and short sentences that sum up important facts and ideas. When taking notes, follow these guidelines:

- Create subject headings and use them to organize your notes.
- Include only the most important information on the topic.
- Write notes in your own words.
- Keep your notes short. Use abbreviations and key phrases that you will recognize.

Write the name of your topic for your investigation. Look through some of the resources you have chosen for your investigation, such as an almanac or magazine. Select two and write notes from these resources. Create subheadings for your notes to help you organize and classify different types of information.

The title of my topic is: _____

1. Resource title:

_____

_____

Notes:

_____

_____

_____

_____

_____

_____

2. Resource title:

_____

_____

Notes:

_____

_____

_____

_____

_____

_____

_____

_____

_____

_____

_____

_____

_____

_____

_____

_____

Writing: Describing Plot

Think

Problem: What is the conflict in the story?

_____

Resolution: How will the conflict be resolved?

_____

Prewriting Use the pyramid diagram below to visually structure your plot. Remember to start at the base, work up to the climax, and then go back down the pyramid where the conflict will be resolved.

Climax

Rising action   Falling action

Beginning   End

_____   _____
(conflict introduced)   (conflict resolved)

Revising

Use this checklist to revise your plot description.

☐ Does your plot have a beginning, a middle, a climax, and an ending?

☐ Did you introduce the problem early on to grab your readers' attention?

☐ Did you clearly identify the main events of the plot, their causes, and the influence of each event on future actions?

Editing

Use this checklist to correct mistakes. Use proofreader's marks as you read your first draft.

☐ Make sure that all words are spelled correctly, even if you have used a computer's spell-check program.

☐ Check all punctuation to make sure that it is correct.

☐ Make sure that sentences and proper nouns begin with capital letters.

Publishing

Use this checklist to get ready for publication.

☐ Give your composition a title that will catch your readers' attention.

☐ Write or type a neat final copy.

☐ Include illustrations and photographs to show your readers what your plot is about. Present them neatly by pasting them onto a sheet of paper or by scanning and placing them in your electronic file.

☐ Share your plot with the rest of the class. See if any of your classmates' plots are similar. How might yours be different?

Prefix *un-* and Suffix *-ous*

Focus

- Remember that prefixes are added to the beginning of base words.

- The **prefix *un-*** is featured in many words. It means "not," or "the opposite of." This prefix will not change the base word's part of speech.

- Remember that suffixes are added to the end of root or base words.

- The **suffix *-ous*** means "full of" or "characterized by." This suffix will usually change nouns into adjectives.

Practice   Add the prefix *un-* to each of the following base words to make a spelling word.

1. certain _____

2. clear _____

3. selfish _____

4. common _____

5. real _____

6. stable _____

7. tangle _____

Word List

1. adventurous
2. courageous
3. dangerous
4. famous
5. glorious
6. mountainous
7. mysterious
8. nervous
9. unable
10. uncertain
11. unclear
12. uncommon
13. undone
14. unequal
15. unlock
16. unpack
17. unreal
18. unselfish
19. unsteady
20. untangle

Challenge Words

21. hazardous
22. monstrous
23. unstable

Add the suffix -ous to each of the following base words to make a spelling word.

8. courage _____

9. danger _____

10. hazard _____

11. nerve _____

12. glory _____

13. mountain _____

Apply Write the spelling word next to its meaning clue.

14. the opposite of lock _____

15. not able _____

16. not equal _____

17. not steady _____

18. the opposite of pack _____

19. the opposite of done _____

Select the correct word from the parentheses that completes each sentence, and write it on the line.

20. My favorite book has a few (mystery, mysterious)

_____ acting characters.

21. If I keep practicing, someday I might be a (fame, famous)

_____ singer.

22. Every time we go on a long hike, it is a huge (adventure, adventurous)

_____.

Verbs

Focus
- Tell students that an **action verb** shows what the subject does. The action can be seen or unseen. For example: Molly *thought* about her idea.
- A **linking verb** does not show action. Linking verbs connect the subject of a sentence with a noun or an adjective that renames or describes the subject. For example: Austin *is* a good golfer.

Practice   Fill in the blank with an action verb.

1. Fran _____ down the hallway as fast as she could.

2. Jupiter _____ faster than Earth.

3. A volcano _____ just miles away from our island resort.

4. Sam _____ a bird feeder out of craft sticks.

5. Audrey _____ up and down on one foot.

6. John _____ higher than anyone else.

7. Hannah _____ her arm in two places.

8. Our teacher _____ this week's novel to us.

9. Trina _____ at the photograph on the wall.

10. Brian _____ tennis with his friends after school.

The following paragraphs contain several verb phrases. Circle each verb phrase. Underline the helping verb. Double underline the main verb.

Danny and Paul were walking their dogs in the park. It was their favorite way to spend Saturday mornings. The day was beautiful.

"Which path should we take?" Danny asked.

There were three paths. They usually took the longest one.

"We could try a new path this time," said Paul.

They did take the new path. It quickly became their favorite trail.

Apply **Each of the following sentences contains a linking verb. Circle the linking verb in each sentence. Then draw an arrow from the subject of the sentence to the noun or adjective it is connected to by the linking verb.**

11. The new teacher seems kind.

12. Scientists are still confused about the results of the experiment.

13. Your dog is quite large.

14. The two friends were inseparable.

15. Jeffrey was hungry after a long day.

16. My mom is pleased with my grades this quarter.

17. Justin looks really sad today.

18. I am a student at West Creek Elementary.

Greek Root *bio* and Suffix *-ist*

 **Focus**
- English words often contain parts, or roots, that have been borrowed from the ancient Greek language.
- When you know the meaning of a **Greek root**, you can begin to figure out the meaning of the English word that contains it.
- One of the common Greek roots is *bio,* which means "life."
- The word *biography* has the Greek roots *bio* and *graph,* which mean "life" and "write." You can tell by the Greek roots that a *biography* is something written about life.
- The **Suffix -*ist*** means "one who practices."

 **Practice**   **Answer the following questions in complete sentences.**

1. What is the root word in biochemistry?

_____

2. What does the root mean?

_____

3. Name another word that contains this root. Use a dictionary if necessary.

_____

_____

Write the base word for each of the following words.

4. hobbyist _____

5. violinist _____

6. accompanist _____

 Add the suffix *-ist* to the base words below, and define the word that is formed.

7. biology _____

8. clarinet _____

9. vocal _____

10. essay _____

11. mural _____

12. type _____

Read each sentence below. Circle the word that you think best completes each sentence.

13. Scientists in Tucson, Arizona, tried to grow a habitat within a

_____. **biosphere / biography**

14. A _____ relationship is when the animals or plants involved benefit one another. **symbiotic / biodegradable**

15. There are many interesting _____ written on Abraham Lincoln. **biographies / antibiotics**

16. A _____ is a large community of diverse animal and plant life within a region. **biochip / biome**

17. *The Diary of a Young Girl* by Anne Frank is a famous _____. **autobiography / biograph**

18. We recycle plastic and glass because they are not _____. **biodegradable / biometric**

Selection Vocabulary

Focus

practical (prak' ti kəl) *adj.* concerned with ordinary activities, business, or work (page 85)

stubborn (stub' ərn) *adj.* unwilling to change (page 85)

tensely (tents' lē) *adv.* feeling emotional strain (page 85)

opportunities (o' pûr tōō' nə tēz) *n.* plural of **opportunity:** a chance to succeed in life (page 87)

crumpled (krum' pəld) *v.* past tense of **crumple:** to press or crush into wrinkles (page 89)

decent (dē' sənt) *adj.* good enough to make someone comfortable (page 91)

concerned (kən sûrnd') *adj.* showing worry (page 93)

biology (bī ol' ə jē) *n.* the study of the way in which plants and animals and other living things live and grow (page 93)

glumly (glum' lē) *adv.* sadly and quietly (page 93)

preoccupied (prē' ä' kyə pīd) *adj.* paying attention to something else (page 93)

success (sək ses') *n.* the achievement of an aim or purpose (page 94)

strive (strīv) *v.* to work to get something (page 94)

Practice   **Write the vocabulary word that best matches the underlined word or phrase in the sentences below.**

1. Kate and her brother argued <u>feeling emotional strain.</u> _____

2. Will your pay at the store be <u>good enough to make you comfortable?</u>

_____

3. Your dad was <u>showing worry</u> when you did not come home on time.

_____

4. "I can't come to your party," Jenny said <u>sadly and quietly.</u> _____

5. I look forward to many great <u>chances to succeed in life.</u>

_____

6. You should always <u>work</u> to do your best. _____

7. Rachel is _____ that the package will not arrive on time.

    a. concerned   **b.** strive   **c.** crumpled

8. _____ comes to those who work hard and stay focused.

    a. Decent   **b.** Success   **c.** Biology

9. I listened _____ as my two best friends argued back and forth.

    a. tensely   **b.** strive   **c.** opportunities

10. If you _____ for an A on your test, I know you can do it.

    a. stubborn   **b.** concerned   **c.** strive

11. A college education will give you many _____ for a good job.

    a. success   **b.** decent   **c.** opportunities

12. Ian is hoping to earn a _____ amount of money this summer.

    a. decent   **b.** concerned   **c.** tensely

13. Laura's father is _____ when discussing her curfew.

    a. crumpled   **b.** stubborn   **c.** glumly

14. He _____ the paper before throwing it in the trash can.

    a. crumpled   **b.** concerned   **c.** strive

Author's Purpose

Focus The **author's purpose** is the main reason for presenting a story or selection in a certain way. An author's purpose

- can be to *inform*, to *explain*, to *entertain*, or to *persuade*.
- affects things in the story, such as the *details, descriptions, story events,* and *dialogue*.

An author can have more than one purpose for writing.

Practice **Read each paragraph below. Pay attention to details and story events. Then write the author's purpose: to inform, to explain, to entertain, or to persuade.**

1. I thought balancing a gumdrop on my nose was a pretty good idea. What I didn't know was that the gumdrop had just fallen off my sister's gingerbread house. It had fresh glue on it. I balanced it all the way through two songs on the radio. I think I invented a new dance!

Purpose: _____

2. If the Elm Street playground is closed, hundreds of families will be affected. Children need a safe place to play. Without the playground they will be forced to use sidewalks and streets for their games. We cannot let the playground be closed.

Purpose: _____

3. Solar energy is much more efficient than many of the energy sources we currently depend upon. It can be converted directly into other forms of energy, such as heat and electricity. For example, solar energy can be used to heat water for use in homes, buildings, and even swimming pools. Solar power can also heat greenhouses, homes, and other buildings.

Purpose: _____

Read the title of each story below. Then write what the author's purpose might be for writing the story—to *inform*, to *explain*, to *entertain*, or to *persuade*.

4. *The Dog That Ate New York*

Author's purpose: _____

5. *Water Safety for Swimming Pool Owners*

Author's purpose: _____

6. *The Care and Feeding of Mice*

Author's purpose: _____

7. *Why You Should Vote*

Author's purpose: _____

8. *My Mother, the Time Traveler*

Author's purpose: _____

Apply   **Write your own paragraph with the purpose of *informing* your readers of something.**

_____

_____

_____

_____

_____

_____

Maps and Atlases

Map A

Map B

Write four questions about either Map A or Map B. Give your questions to a classmate. When your classmate has finished answering them, discuss the questions. Share how maps could be useful in your research project for this or other units.

1. _____

_____

2. _____

_____

3. _____

_____

4. _____

_____

In the box, draw a map of one of the following: your city/town, your state, or your region of the country. Use a map or atlas to help you accurately plot cities, landforms, or landmarks. Draw a scale that shows how many miles are represented by inches on your map. Then write six questions about your map for a classmate to answer. Discuss the questions together.

5. _____

6. _____

7. _____

8. _____

9. _____

10. _____

Writing a Story

Think Think of the dream Langston Hughes had in the selection. Write a story about a dream you have and how you would work to make it a reality.

Audience: Who will be your audience for this story?

_____

Purpose: What is your reason for writing this story?

_____

Prewriting Fill in the important details of your narrative in the story map below. Write any additional sensory details in the margins of the page or in your Writer's Notebook.

Title: _____

_____

Characters: _____

_____

Setting: _____

_____

Plot Beginning: _____

_____

Middle: _____

_____

Climax: _____

_____

End: _____

_____

Revising   Use this checklist to revise your story.

☐ Does your plot have a beginning, a middle, a climax, and an ending?

☐ Did you use plenty of concrete sensory details?

☐ Does your story capture your readers' attention and keep it until the end?

Editing   Use this checklist to correct mistakes. Use proofreader's marks as you read your first draft.

☐ Make sure that all words are spelled correctly.

☐ Check all punctuation to make sure that it is correct.

☐ Make sure that sentences and proper nouns begin with capital letters.

Publishing   Use this checklist to get ready for publication.

☐ Give your composition a title that will catch your readers' attention.

☐ Write or type a neat final copy.

☐ Read your work one more time. Correct any errors.

☐ You can bind your work into a book and keep a copy in your classroom for others to read.

☐ Compile all of your classmates' stories into a literary journal that can be placed in your classroom or the school library.

☐ Read your story aloud to your classmates or to younger students.

Greek Root *bio* and Suffix *-ist*

Focus

- Many English words contain **Greek roots.**
- If you know the spellings and meanings of common Greek roots, you can figure out how to spell and define words that contain the roots.
- The **Greek root *bio*** means "life."
- Remember that suffixes are added to the end of base words.
- The **suffix *-ist*** means "one who practices." Words with this suffix will usually be nouns.

Practice Underline the Greek root *bio* in these spelling words.

1. biochip

2. biomass

3. biorhythm

4. bionic

5. antibiotic

Word List

1. antibiotic
2. autobiography
3. bicyclist
4. biochemistry
5. biochip
6. biological
7. biomass
8. bionic
9. biotechnology
10. economist
11. extremist
12. futurist
13. journalist
14. microbiology
15. motorist
16. optimist
17. organist
18. pianist
19. specialist
20. theorist

Challenge Words

21. archivist
22. biorhythm
23. symbiotic

Add the suffix -ist to each of these base words to make a spelling word.

6. motor _____

7. special _____

8. extreme _____

9. organ _____

10. future _____

Apply Correct the spelling of each word and write it on the line. If the word is already correct, write correct.

11. biological _____

12. biocyclist _____

13. pianest _____

14. journalist _____

15. autobiography _____

16. optimmist _____

17. symbiotic _____

18. economyist _____

19. archiveist _____

20. microbialogy _____

Pronouns

**Focus**
- A **pronoun** is used in place of one or more nouns.
- Like nouns, pronouns can be subjects or objects in a sentence.
  - A pronoun that receives the action of the verb is the direct object. (The cat chased **it.**)
  - A pronoun after a preposition is the object of the preposition. (The bird flew over **me.**)
- **Personal pronouns** name specific people or things.
- **Personal object pronouns** are *me, you, him, her, it, us, you,* and *them.*

Practice   **In each of the following sentences, the object is underlined. On the line, write a personal object pronoun to replace the noun(s).**

1. Kerry was born before <u>James</u> was. _____

2. I lost <u>my wallet</u> at the amusement park. _____

3. I wanted to tell <u>Claire and Lola</u> the good news. _____

4. Viv was nervous about reading her paper to <u>Phoebe and me</u>. _____

5. The two girls sat down beside <u>Mrs. Gibbon</u>. _____

6. I read <u>the whole book</u> in one day. _____

7. Jenny will meet <u>Alex and me</u> at the movie theater. _____

8. I am not sure whether my sister will talk to <u>John</u>. _____

9. The ball landed near <u>Willie and Bob</u>. _____

10. I knitted a sweater for <u>my grandmother</u>. _____

Read this paragraph. The pronouns are missing. Write the correct pronoun in each blank so the paragraph makes sense.

Justin and Arlena were sure that the hot-air balloon was moving faster than

_____ thought it should be. Arlena looked at Justin and told

_____ that _____ wasn't scared. Justin said that

_____ wasn't scared either. Although neither one of

_____ was scared, _____ agreed to keep

talking to each other. Finally, the pilot of the balloon said, "It's time for

_____ to land."

Read this paragraph. If an underlined pronoun is incorrect, write the correct pronoun above it. If it is correct, write the word "correct" above it.

The strange men left <u>their</u> enormous wooden boats and waded toward

shore. This was the first time that <u>us</u> had seen these people, and <u>us</u> weren't

sure what <u>them</u> wanted. <u>We</u> asked one another, "Who are these men? Why are

<u>them</u> here? What are those things in <u>theirs</u> hands?" <u>We</u> will soon see what

<u>it</u> want, <u>me</u> thought.

Superlative Adjectives and Adverbs

- **Superlatives** are adjectives and adverbs that compare three or more things.

- Superlative adjectives compare three or more *nouns.*

- Superlative adverbs compare three or more *verbs.*

Most superlatives end in *-est.*

- Adjective: Tran is the **tallest** girl in her family.

- Adverb: Beth swims the butterfly **fastest** of any of her teammates.

Sometimes we add *most* to form the superlatives. In these cases, **do not** add *-est.*

- Adjective: The puzzle was the **most challenging** one that Lisa had ever put together.

- Adverb: Sean is the one who can type the **most skillfully** in our group.

Some adjectives and adverbs have different superlative forms.

- Adjectives with different superlative forms include *good, bad,* and *many.*

- Her grandmother's soup is the **best** in town.

- Adverbs with different superlative forms include *well, badly, much,* and *little.*

- Of all the family members, Tia plays video games the **least.**

Practice Read the sentences. Circle the correct superlative for each adjective.

1. Which amusement park is (biggest/most big), Splash City, Waterfest, or World of Fun?

2. World of Fun has the (scariest/most scary) roller coaster that I've ever ridden.

3. The (oldest/most old) wooden roller coaster in the world is located at World of Fun.

4. There is a water slide at World of Fun that is the (highest/most high) slide in all of California.

Read the sentences. Circle the correct superlative for each adverb.

5. Will was the person in our group waiting (patientest/most patiently) for his sandwich.

6. Will and Randy performed (best/most well) in the talent show.

7. Tara said she'd rather see which frog could jump (highest/most high) in the frog jumping contest.

 **Apply**   **Read the sentences. Write the superlative form of each word in parentheses in the blank at the end of each sentence.**

8. Box turtles live the (long) of any animal on our planet. _____

9. The (important) thing to remember is your raincoat.   _____

10. Today is the (bad) day Tina has had all week.   _____

11. Sue cheered (loudly) of anyone in the crowd.   _____

12. Jon's baseball collection is the (big) collection in town. _____

13. Leslie describes scenes the (well) out of anyone in our writing group.

_____

14. I made the (few) mistakes possible when I wrote my paper.

_____

15. Gary claimed that the last book in the series was the (interesting).

_____

16. Our football stadium is the (large) in the state. _____

Selection Vocabulary

Focus

island (ī' lənd) *n.* an area of land surrounded by water and smaller than a continent (page 104)

brilliant (bril' yənt) *adj.* bright (page 104)

luxurious (lug' zhŏŏr' ē əs) *adj.* rich and comfortable (page 104)

drooping (drŏŏp' ing) *v.* form of **droop:** to hang or sink down; sag (page 106)

courtyards (kort' yärdz) *n.* plural of **courtyard:** an open space exposed to the sky, especially one enclosed on all sides (page 106)

nudged (nujd) *v.* past tense of **nudge:** to push slightly (page 107)

crowed (krōd) *v.* past tense of **crow:** to brag loudly (page 107)

astonishment (ə ston' ish mənt) *n.* great surprise; amazement (page 107)

shrill (shril) *adj.* having a sharp high-pitched tone (page 108)

history (his' tə rē) *n.* a chronological record of significant events (page 108)

jeered (jērd) *v.* past tense of **jeer:** to abuse vocally; to taunt (page 108)

plume (plüm) *n.* a big fluffy feather (page 108)

Practice   Write the vocabulary word next to the group of words that have a similar meaning.

1. sagging; bending; slouching _____

2. wonder; amazement; surprise _____

3. mocked; put down; sneered _____

4. prodded; poked; pushed _____

5. lush; rich; abundant _____

6. boasted; bragged; flaunted _____

7. sparkling; bright; radiant _____

8. Someone was proud of an accomplishment and told everyone about it.

What did he do? _____

9. A person might have this reaction to a surprise birthday party.

What is it? _____

10. The stars are sparkling and shining brightly tonight.

What are they? _____

11. The fabric on the new chair was made of soft, expensive velvet.

What was it? _____

12. The plant has not been watered since last week.

What is it probably doing? _____

13. Josiah gently pushed his sister forward in line.

What did he do to her? _____

14. Teron had a big fluffy feather on his hat.

What is another word for what he had? _____

15. I took a boat to an area of land surrounded by water on all sides.

Where did I go? _____

16. The scholar was studying the background and events leading up to the fall of Roman civilization.

What was the scholar studying? _____

17. When the politician failed to fulfill his campaign promises, the crowd taunted him.

What did they do? _____

18. The eagle let out a sharp, high-pitched cry as it dove into the valley.

What kind of cry was it? _____

Writing: Responding to Literature

 **Think** about the aspects of a story—the setting, the characters, and the plot.

Did all these work in the story you have read? If not, why?

_____

What could have been changed to further enhance the story?

_____

 After you have read "Daedalus and Icarus" (or another fictional story you have recently read), answer the following questions to demonstrate your understanding of the text.

What are the main ideas? _____

_____

Who are the main characters? _____

_____

What are the key events of the story? _____

_____

What images did the writing create in your mind? _____

_____

What did you like most about the selection, and why? _____

_____

If you could ask the author one question about the selection,

what would it be? _____

_____

What prior experiences influenced how you understood the story? _____

_____

Revising

Use this checklist to revise your literary response.

☐ Is your opening paragraph cogent (compelling and convincing)?

☐ Did you go back and add details where needed?

☐ Did you support each of your judgments or opinions through references to the text or prior experience?

Editing

Use this checklist to correct mistakes. Use proofreader's marks as you read your first draft.

☐ Make sure that all words are spelled correctly.

☐ Check all punctuation to make sure that it is correct.

☐ Make sure that sentences and proper nouns begin with capital letters.

Publishing

Use this checklist to get ready for publication.

☐ Write or type a neat final copy.

☐ Read your work one more time. Correct any errors.

☐ Share your response to literature with others. You and your classmates can bind your responses together as a literary journal. This journal could be placed in the school library or kept in the classroom for others to read.

Superlatives and Suffix *-ment*

Focus
- **Superlatives** are words that end in **-est.**
- Superlatives are adjectives and adverbs that are used to compare more than two things.
- Adding *-est* may require changes to the base word. Sometimes the *y* at the end of a base word changes to *i* before adding *-est.*
- The **suffix -ment** means "the act or process of," "the state of being," or "the result of."
- This suffix usually changes verbs into nouns.

Practice Sort the following spelling words under the correct heading.

arrangement	boldest	amendment
establishment	fewest	easiest
placement	employment	dirtiest
disappointment	largest	

Superlatives

1. _____
2. _____
3. _____
4. _____
5. _____

Suffix -ment

6. _____
7. _____
8. _____
9. _____
10. _____
11. _____

Word List
1. achievement
2. advertisement
3. amusement
4. arrangement
5. boldest
6. calmest
7. coolest
8. dirtiest
9. disappointment
10. easiest
11. employment
12. enjoyment
13. fewest
14. funniest
15. government
16. largest
17. newest
18. placement
19. refreshment
20. youngest

Challenge Words
21. amendment
22. establishment
23. predicament

 **Apply** Write the spelling word next to its meaning clue.

12. the act or process of being governed _____

13. most calm _____

14. the act or process of advertising _____

15. most new _____

16. most young _____

Circle the words that are spelled correctly.

17. funniest   funnyiest

18. predicement   predicament

19. amusment   amusement

20. achievement   achevement

Objects

Focus

- An **object** is a noun or pronoun in a sentence that is related to a verb or a preposition.

- A **direct object** is a noun or pronoun that receives the action of a verb. To identify a direct object, find the verb, and then ask *whom* or *what*. The answer is the direct object; for example: Danielle called *me* yesterday.

- An **indirect object** is a noun or pronoun for whom or to whom something is done. To find the indirect object, ask *to whom*, *to what*, *for whom*, or *for what* after you locate the verb. The answer is the indirect object; for example: The teachers gave *us* an end-of-the-year party.

- A preposition is a word that relates a noun or a pronoun to some other word in the sentence. A preposition cannot stand alone. It must have an object. The **object of the preposition** is the noun or pronoun that follows a preposition in a sentence; for example: She read the book on the *table*.

Practice

In the following sentences, determine whether the underlined words are direct objects, indirect objects, or objects of the prepositions. On the line, write D for direct, I for indirect, and P for object of the preposition.

1. Michael rode a lime green <u>bike</u>. _____

2. Jim told his <u>classmates</u> a joke. _____

3. The painter sketched a <u>drawing</u>. _____

4. The best hiding spot is in the <u>basement</u>. _____

5. Jasmine finished her science <u>project</u>. _____

6. The orange cat sits on the <u>fence</u>. _____

7. We made our <u>father</u> breakfast. _____

8. That tree almost fell on <u>him</u>. _____

9. Matthew always drinks <u>water</u>. _____

10. Traci gave <u>Sam</u> her backpack to hold. _____

Apply — **In the following sentences, underline the verb, circle the direct objects or objects of the prepositions.**

11. Josh ate his banana.

12. Alan threw the baseball.

13. My dog chased the cat.

14. The carpenter made a hutch.

15. Theresa likes her classmates.

16. The cow jumped over the fence.

17. The car drove over the bridge.

18. The board games are inside the closet.

19. Jennifer walked outside with her sister.

20. Shannon ducked beneath the covers.

Compound Words

Focus

A **compound word** is a word that is made up of two or more smaller words. *(playmate, timetable)*

A word with a prefix or suffix is not compound. *(unfair, played)*

Compounds can be open, closed, or hyphenated.

An **open compound** is two separate words. Example: **high school**

A **closed compound** is combined into one word. Example: **loudspeaker**

A **hyphenated compound** connects two words with a hyphen. Example: **first-class**

Use a dictionary to find out if a compound word is **open, closed,** or **hyphenated.**

Practice

Write the following sets of words as compounds. Read the clue in parentheses to find out how to write the word correctly.

1. warm, blooded (hyphenated) _____

2. air, plane (closed) _____

3. tail, gate (closed) _____

4. trash, can (open) _____

5. billy, goat (open) _____

6. empty, handed (hyphenated) _____

7. clean, cut (hyphenated) _____

8. ship, wreck (closed) _____

Apply   Circle the compound word in each sentence. On the line, write what kind of compound it is (open, closed, or hyphenated).

9. When I hurt my arm, it took a lot of self-control to keep from crying.

_____

10. Is there a difference between a hedgehog and a porcupine?

_____

11. We always have to return our textbooks at the end of the year.

_____

12. There was a sweet-smelling scent coming from the bakery on the corner.

_____

13. My favorite player hit a grand slam last night to win the game.

_____

14. I painted the entire background blue to represent the sky.

_____

15. When it comes to gardening, my aunt has a green thumb.

_____

Write a sentence using each of the following compound words.

16. birdbath _____

_____

17. daylight _____

_____

18. empty-handed _____

_____

Selection Vocabulary

 **Focus**

jagged (ja' gəd) *adj.* having sharp points that stick out (page 128)

droplet (dräp' lət) *n.* a tiny drop of liquid (page 128)

trickled (tri' kəld) *v.* past tense of **trickle:** to run slowly in a series of drops or a thin stream (page 129)

flowed (flōd) *v.* past tense of **flow:** to move as water does (page 129)

brook (brŏŏk) *n.* a small natural stream of freshwater (page 130)

irrigation (ir' ə gā' shən) *n.* having to do with supplying farmland with water (page 131)

torrent (tôr' ənt) *n.* a fast, heavy stream of water or other liquid (page 132)

reservoir (re' zə vwär') *n.* a lake, often artificial, for storing water (page 132)

particles (pär' ti kəlz) *n.* plural of **particle:** a tiny piece (page 132)

raging (ra' jing) *adj.* violent; wild (page 135)

condensing (kən dens' ing) *v.* form of **condense:** to make or become less in size or volume (page 136)

glacier (glā' shûr) *n.* a huge mass of ice formed from unmelted snow, usually found in the polar regions or in high mountains (page 136)

Practice **Write the vocabulary word that best matches the underlined word or phrase in the sentences below.**

1. I took a picture of the <u>huge mass of ice</u> from our ship's window.

_____

2. The stream <u>moved as water does</u> down the mountain. _____

3. They walked around the <u>lake that stores water</u> three times.

_____

4. The mountain had several <u>sharp-pointed</u> peaks. _____

5. The water <u>ran slowly</u> out of the faucet. _____

6. The new <u>water-supplying system</u> on my uncle's farm uses advanced

technology. _____

Write the word from the word box that matches each definition below.

jagged	particles	flowed	reservoir
trickled	glacier	irrigation	raging

7. _____ a huge piece of slowly moving, compacted snow

8. _____ a lake for storing water

9. _____ moved as water does

10. _____ ran in a series of drops

11. _____ violent; wild

12. _____ watering crops or land artificially

13. _____ small pieces of solid matter

14. _____ having pointed, sharp notches

Apply Write a sentence using at least one of the vocabulary words from this lesson.

15. _____

_____

_____

Sequence

 Focus   **Sequence** is the order of events in a story. Writers often use signal words called time-and-order words to help readers follow the action in a story.

Time-and-order words show

- the **order** in which events take place. Words such as *first, then, so, when,* and *finally* show order.

- the passage of **time** in a story. Words such as *spring, tomorrow,* and *morning* show time.

Practice   **Look through "The Snowflake: A Water Cycle Story." Find sentences with time and order words. Write the words along with a *T* next to the word if it shows time or an *O* if it shows order. Then explain how these words help you understand the sequence of events in the story.**

1. Word: _____   Time/Order _____

2. Word: _____   Time/Order _____

3. Word: _____   Time/Order _____

4. Word: _____   Time/Order _____

5. Word: _____   Time/Order _____

How do these words help you understand the sequence of events in the story?

6. _____

_____

Read the following sentences. Fill in the spaces with words that signal time or order.

7. _____ the bank is open from 9:00 A.M. to 5:00 P.M.

8. It closes at 3:00 P.M. _____.

9. _____ is a holiday, so the bank will be closed all day.

10. The _____ stop on the tour was the old Post Office.

11. _____ we visited the theater.

12. _____ lunch we saw the library.

13. This _____, I expect my mother's tulips to bloom.

14. When I went to the store _____, I forgot to get milk.

Apply   **Write a short paragraph about an ordinary day in your life. Use time and order words in your paragraph.**

_____

_____

_____

_____

_____

_____

_____

_____

Parts of a Book

Understanding the parts of a book will help you find information faster because you will know where to look. Some books, but not all, have these parts.

These pages are at the front of many books:

- The **title page** gives the title of the book, the names of the author or editor and the illustrator, and the name of the publisher.

- The **copyright page** gives the publisher's name and the place and year the book was published.

- The **table of contents** lists, in numerical order, the units, chapters, or stories in the book with the page number on which each item begins.

These pages are at the back of many books:

- The **index** is an alphabetical list in the back of the book of important names and subjects and the pages on which they appear.

- The **bibliography** is a list of books, newspapers, magazines, and other resources that the author used for information.

- The **glossary** is an alphabetical list of special words used in the book and their definitions.

Use books from the library or your classroom to answer these questions.

1. Complete the following about a fiction book that contains this information.

Title: _____

Author: _____

Illustrator: _____

Copyright date: _____

Where can you find the name of the publisher? _____

_____

Where can you find a list of the units and chapter titles in a book?

_____

2. Complete the following about a nonfiction book that contains this information.

Title: _____

Copyright date: _____

Author(s) or Editor(s): _____

Illustrator or Photographer: _____

What is the title of the first chapter? _____

The first chapter begins on which page? _____

Based on the chapter title, what is Chapter 1 about? _____

_____

These four entries and page numbers are listed in the index.

_____

_____

_____

_____

These four words and their meanings are from the glossary.

_____

_____

_____

Compound Words and Suffix *-al*

Focus

- **Compound Words** are words made by combining two or more smaller words. If you know the meanings of the two smaller words, you can usually figure out the meaning of the compound word that they create.

- For example, *springtime* is the time when spring occurs.

- Remember that **suffixes** are one or more letters added to the end of a base word. The spelling of the base word often changes when adding the suffix.

- The **suffix *-al*** means "relating to" or "like," and adding the suffix *-al* changes nouns to adjectives.

- For example, *social* refers to something relating to society.

Practice   Write the spelling word next to its meaning.

1. related to the horizon _____

2. having to do with directions _____

3. used in agriculture _____

4. relating to doctors and medicine _____

5. having to do with numerical digits _____

6. involving a likeliness to judge harshly _____

7. relating to magazines and journals _____

8. relating to reason and understanding _____

Word List

1. agricultural
2. airplane
3. background
4. birdbath
5. daylight
6. departmental
7. digital
8. directional
9. doorstep
10. emotional
11. greenhouse
12. homeroom
13. horizontal
14. instructional
15. medical
16. overcast
17. overlook
18. sandbox
19. scrapbook
20. watercolor

Challenge Words

21. judgmental
22. periodical
23. rational

Write all of the spelling words that are compound words.

9. _____

10. _____

11. _____

12. _____

13. _____

14. _____

15. _____

16. _____

17. _____

18. _____

19. _____

20. _____

Apply   Circle the misspelled words in the sentence below.
Then write each word correctly.

The plants in the grenhouze were not growing well because the ovrkast sky was

not leting in the daylite.

21. _____

22. _____

23. _____

24. _____

Simple Sentences

 Focus

A **simple sentence** has a subject and a predicate. The predicate can be a verb or a verb phrase.

Example:

Simple sentence with a verb: Micah <u>went</u> to the library.

Simple sentence with a verb phrase: Our cousins <u>are coming</u> to our house.

 **Practice**

Circle the subject in each sentence. Underline the verb or verb phrase.

1. Zoe walked to the store.

2. Tonio and Mike were going to the park.

3. Skyscrapers are very tall.

4. Those dogs are having fun.

5. This is my favorite game.

6. Bridget went to Elizabeth's house.

Fill in the missing words in the simple sentences below.

7. _____ can play with me today.

8. The gold necklace _____ brightly.

9. The wind _____ the clouds across the sky.

10. The _____ twinkle like diamonds.

11. The phone _____.

12. The _____ on the trees _____ in autumn.

13. The _____ _____ a nest in the tree.

14. The thunderstorm _____ fast.

15. This canteen _____ a lot of water.

16. The rocket _____ soared across the sky.

17. _____ likes to study genealogy.

18. Tabitha _____ the monument for her art project.

Apply A student wrote the story below for homework. Circle the subject, and underline the verb in each sentence. Then answer the questions.

My Muddy Day

I took my dog to the park. He jumped in a big puddle. Muddy water covered him. He came running back to me. Then he shook his fur.

19. How many simple sentences are in the story? _____

20. How do you know they are simple sentences?

_____

_____

_____

_____

_____

Grammar, Usage, and Mechanics • *Skills Practice 1*

Inflectional Ending -ed

 **Focus**
- The inflectional ending *-ed* indicates a past action.
- Some words require you to drop the silent e before you add *-ed*; for example: dance, danced.

Practice **Change the following words using *-ed* to indicate a past action.**

1. sway _____

2. dance _____

3. agree _____

4. notice _____

5. perform _____

6. move _____

7. want _____

8. wonder _____

9. I (looked, lookd) _____ past the gate and saw that the movers were already here for our things.

10. Julia was (inclineed, inclined) _____ to sell pencils at school as a fund-raiser.

11. I am glad my teacher (encouragd, encouraged) _____ me to join the math competition.

12. By having people vote, we realized the (favored, favord)

    _____ option was to go outside for recess.

13. When Brian realized that he had (computeed, computed)

    _____ incorrectly, he started the problem over from the beginning.

14. Brian (followed, followd) _____ me to the bus stop to say goodbye.

15. José (obtaind, obtained) _____ his job easily because he was qualified.

16. The hurricane was (expected, expectid) _____ to devastate the city.

Selection Vocabulary

Focus

energy (e' nûr jē) *n.* the power to do work (page 146)

transferred (trants fûrd') *v.* past tense of **transfer:** to pass along (page 147)

windmills (wind' milz') *n.* plural of **windmill:** a machine that uses the power of wind to grind grain or produce electrical power (page 147)

soar (sor) *v.* to fly high (page 147)

release (ri lēs') *v.* to let loose (page 148)

fuels (fū' əlz) *n.* plural of **fuel:** something that gives out energy as it is burned (page 148)

stored (stord) *adj.* past tense of **store:** to put away for future use (page 148)

contains (kən tānz') *v.* form of **contain:** to hold (page 149)

eventually (i vent' shə wə lē) *adv.* sooner or later (page 150)

remains (ri mānz') *n.* things that are left (page 151)

creates (krē āts') *v.* form of **create:** to make (page 152)

trace (trās) *n.* a small piece or a sign left behind showing that something was there (page 155)

Practice Circle the correct word that completes each sentence.

1. The baby eagle quickly learned to _____.

    a. release   **b.** soar   **c.** stored

2. Riley decided to _____ her pet turtle into the wild.

    a. contains   **b.** stored   **c.** release

3. I do not have enough _____ to run two miles tonight.

    a. energy   **b.** contains   **c.** transferred

4. If you don't water those plants, they will _____ die.

    a. eventually   **b.** soar   **c.** stored

5. Many _____ are found naturally under the ground.

    a. energy   **b.** stored   **c.** fuels

 **Apply** Match each word on the left to its definition on the right.

6. eventually   **a.** the capacity or ability to work

7. fuels   **b.** holds

8. stored   **c.** sooner or later

9. contains   **d.** saved for future use

10. energy   **e.** to let loose

11. transferred   **f.** things that are burned for energy

12. soar   **g.** to glide high

13. release   **h.** passed along

14. **Fill in each blank with the appropriate vocabulary word to complete the paragraph.**

While waiting in line at the amusement park, I bought some candy. I ate some of it and then _____ the rest in my bag to eat later. We watched the cars _____ up the track and then speed back down. My younger brother was too scared to ride the roller coaster. "You're going to have to get over your fear _____ ," I told him. After the rides, we played miniature golf. If you hit the ball through one of the _____ you get a prize. Then we played some other games. In one game, you had to _____ the quarter just at the right moment so it would roll into the slot. By the end of the day, I was had no more _____, and I was ready to sleep on the way home.

Main Idea and Details

Focus

The **main idea** is what a paragraph is about. Often, a writer provides a clear topic sentence at the beginning of a paragraph.

- The **main idea** is the most important point the writer makes in a paragraph. The main idea tells what the whole paragraph is about.

- **Details** are bits of information in the sentences of paragraphs that support the main idea.

Practice

Find two paragraphs in "Energy Makes Things Happen" that have a clearly stated main idea. Write the page number, main idea, and two details from each paragraph.

1. Page: _____ Main Idea: _____

_____

Detail: _____

_____

Detail: _____

_____

2. Page: _____ Main Idea: _____

_____

Detail: _____

_____

Detail: _____

_____

Read the paragraph. Underline the main idea. Then write two sentences from the paragraph with details that support the main idea.

Casey decided that he wanted to know more about birds. First he got some bird books from the library. Then he made a feeder from a plastic bottle and a hanger. He hung the feeder near the patio in the backyard. When he was done, Casey found a comfortable spot where he could sit and watch the woodpeckers, finches, and other birds that came for food and water.

Detail: _____

_____

Detail: _____

_____

Apply   **Write a paragraph about using energy. State your main idea in the first sentence. Add sentences with details that support the main idea.**

_____

_____

_____

_____

_____

_____

_____

Summarizing and Organizing Information

Summarizing will help you organize information and remember what you have read. When you write a summary, look for the main ideas and important details, and use your own words to tell what happens in the story. Select a story from Unit 1. Write the title on the line below. Summarize the story by filling in the flow chart. Write the main ideas and important details from the story in your own words.

Title: _____

How does the story begin?

_____

_____

_____

↓

What happens next?

_____

_____

↓

What happens after that?

_____

_____

↓

How does the story end?

_____

_____

Summarizing and Organizing Information

Choose a well-known book or movie, but do not put the title of it on the flow chart. Summarize the story on the flow chart. Then, exchange papers with a partner. Guess the title of the book or movie on your partner's flow chart. Write it on the line below.

How does the story begin?

_____

_____

↓

What happens next?

_____

_____

↓

What happens after that?

_____

_____

↓

How does the story end?

_____

_____

Can you guess the title? Write it here.

_____

Title guessed by (name): _____

Writing a Summary

Think

Audience: Who will read your summary?

_____

Purpose: What is your reason for writing a summary?

_____

Prewriting Use this graphic organizer to summarize the expository information you learned in "Energy Makes Things Happen" or another expository article you have recently read. Write the main idea of the story in the center circle and supporting details in the smaller surrounding circles. You may add circles if you have more information.

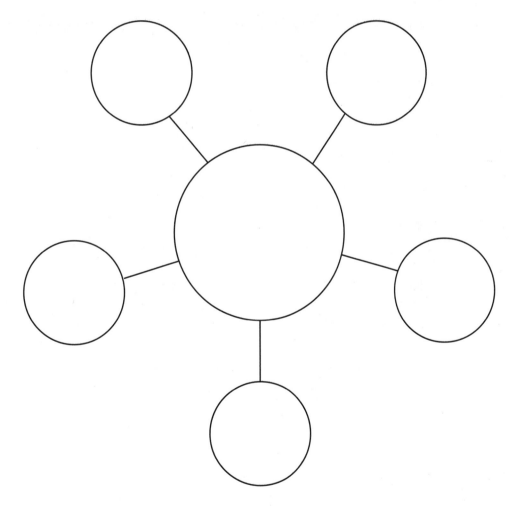

Revising   Use this checklist to revise your summary.

☐ Did you write about the main idea of your selection?

☐ Did you include only the most important details?

☐ Do the other sentences in the paragraphs support the main idea?

Editing   Use this checklist to correct mistakes. Use proofreader's marks as you read your first draft.

☐ Make sure that all words are spelled correctly.

☐ Check all punctuation to make sure that it is correct.

☐ Make sure that sentences and proper nouns begin with capital letters.

☐ Did you use pronouns properly?

Publishing   Use this checklist to get ready for publication.

☐ Write or type a neat final copy.

☐ Read your work one more time. Correct any errors.

☐ Include illustrations and photographs to show your readers what your summary is about. Present them neatly by pasting them onto a sheet of paper or by scanning and placing them in your electronic file.

Prefix *mid-* and Inflectional Ending *-ed*

 **Focus**

- A **prefix** is one or more letters added to the beginning of a base word that changes the word's meaning. Knowing the meaning of the prefix will help you figure out the meanings of unfamiliar words. The **prefix *mid-*** means "middle."

- For example, *midnight* means "in the middle of the night."

- The spelling of base words may change in predictable ways when inflectional endings are added. For many base words, you can add the **inflectional ending *-ed*.**

- When adding the inflectional ending *-ed*, you are referring to something that has already happened.

- For example in the sentence, "I tripped over the branch," the *-ed* indicates the action was already performed.

Practice Sort the spelling words into the categories of the inflectional ending *-ed* and prefix *mid-*.

Inflectional Ending *-ed*

1. _____
2. _____
3. _____
4. _____
5. _____
6. _____
7. _____
8. _____
9. _____
10. _____

Prefix *mid-*

11. _____
12. _____
13. _____
14. _____
15. _____
16. _____
17. _____
18. _____
19. _____
20. _____

Word List

1. absorbed
2. avoided
3. blushed
4. called
5. coated
6. halted
7. heated
8. intended
9. midline
10. midmonth
11. midmorning
12. midrange
13. midsection
14. midsize
15. midsummer
16. midtown
17. midway
18. midyear
19. miscounted
20. thanked

Challenge Words

21. decayed
22. galloped
23. scorched

Write the spelling word next to its meaning clue.

21. to have covered completely _____

22. halfway through the month _____

23. warmed up _____

24. added incorrectly _____

25. not small but not large _____

26. soaked _____

27. turned red or scarlet in color _____

28. shouted or yelled _____

29. the middle of July _____

30. central section of the city _____

Apply   **Circle the correctly spelled words below.**

31. haltedd   haltted   halted

32. midcection   midscetion   midsection

33. entended   inntended   intended

34. avoided   avooided   avoidded

35. decaiyed   decayed   dekayed

36. galloped   gallopped   galoped

37. midlyne   medline   midline

38. midmorning   middmorning   midmourning

39. skorched   scorched   scoreched

40. midweigh   middway   midway

Name _____ Date _____

Types of Sentences

There are simple sentences, compound sentences, and complex sentences.

Type	Example
A **simple sentence** is an independent clause. This type of sentence has a subject and a predicate.	A penny has a picture of Lincoln on one side.
A **compound sentence** is made by joining two simple sentences. The sentences are joined by conjunctions such as *and, or,* or *but.* Put a comma before the conjunction in a compound sentence.	A penny has a picture of Lincoln on one side, and it has the Lincoln Memorial on the other side.
A **complex sentence** has one independent clause and one or more dependent clauses. In some complex sentences, the independent clause is first, followed by the dependent clause. In other complex sentences, the dependent clause is at the beginning of the sentence. Separate an introductory dependent clause from the independent clause with a comma. Remember that an independent clause can be a sentence by itself. A dependent clause cannot be a sentence by itself.	I saw a penny from 1898 when we went to the museum. *The first clause is independent, and the second is dependent.* If you ever find a coin, you can look for the date to find the year it was made. *The first clause is dependent, and the second is independent.*

Practice Decide whether the sentence is simple, compound, or complex. Write *S* for simple, *C* for compound, and *X* for complex.

1. It is hot today. _____

2. My friend and I are going swimming. _____

3. We don't have snow in the winter because it is warm where we live.

_____

4. We will bring our lunches to the park, and we will eat under a tree.

_____

5. If it doesn't rain, we will go swimming tomorrow too. _____

 **Apply** Follow the directions for each sentence.

6. *Change to a compound sentence. Underline the conjunction.* The Nile is the longest river in the world. The Amazon is the second longest

_____

_____

7. *Change to two simple sentences.* Be careful as you walk, because the sidewalk is slippery.

_____

8. *Change to a complex sentence. Underline the dependent clause.* We can fly our kites. It is windy.

_____

9. *Change to a compound sentence. What punctuation mark should you add?* Washington is on a quarter. He is also on a dollar bill.

_____

_____

10. *Change to one simple sentence.* I brought the chair to the table, and I sat down.

_____

11. *Change to a compound sentence. Underline the conjunction.* Snow makes me think of winter. Rain makes me think of spring.

_____

_____

12. *Change to a complex sentence. Underline the dependent clause.* I hear music, and I feel happy.

_____

Homographs

 Focus
- **Homographs** are words that are spelled the same but have different pronunciations and meanings.
- Example: The word *tear* could mean "a drop of moisture from the eye," or it could mean "rip."

Practice   Write two definitions for each homograph.

1. object _____

2. entrance _____

3. conflict _____

_____

4. console _____

_____

5. bass _____

_____

6. live _____

_____

The words in the sentences are underlined because they have different pronunciations and meanings.
Write the meaning of each underlined word in the order they appear in the sentences.

Example: I will <u>present</u> her with a <u>present</u> at the party.

present - to give present - a gift

I will <u>lead</u> you through a tour of the <u>lead</u> mine.

7. _____

8. _____

Did you <u>record</u> her <u>record</u>-breaking jump?

9. _____

10. _____

The girl with the <u>bow</u> in her hair stood on the <u>bow</u> of the ship.

11. _____

12. _____

As the elevator doors <u>close</u>, we realize how <u>close</u> we are to each other.

13. _____

14. _____

Instead of <u>putting</u> my golf clubs away when I lost, I decided to practice my <u>putting</u>.

15. _____

16. _____

Selection Vocabulary

 **Focus**

linked (linkt) *v.* past tense of **link:** to connect (page 164)

food chain (fōōd chān) *n.* a series of living things, in which the first is eaten by the second, the second is eaten by the third, and so on (page 164)

depend (di pend') *v.* to need; to rely (page 168)

food web (fōōd web) *n.* a complex system of food chains (page 170)

bitterly (bi' tûr lē) *adv.* harshly; extremely (page 172)

feast (fēst) *v.* to eat (page 172)

seaweed (sē wēd) *n.* a plant that grows near the surface of the sea (page 174)

harbor (här' bər) *n.* a sheltered place along a coast, where ships and boats often anchor (page 174)

spiny (spīn' ē) *adj.* covered with or having sharp points, as an animal (page 175)

urchins (ûr' chinz) *n.* plural of **urchin:** a spiny sea organism (page 175)

seafloor (sē' flôr) *n.* the bottom of a sea or ocean (page 175)

branch (branch) *v.* to divide and subdivide (page 176)

Practice Write the vocabulary word next to the group of words that have a similar meaning.

1. harshly; extremely; severely _____

2. eat; indulge; treat _____

3. trust; rely; need _____

4. attached; connected; joined _____

5. pointed; sharp; thorny _____

6. divide; spread; offshoot _____

7. kelp; algae; rockweed _____

Apply Fill in each blank with a vocabulary word from this lesson to complete each sentence.

8. _____ is actually quite delicious.

9. Our boat docked at the _____ earlier than we expected.

10. The two girls _____ their arms together and began to skip.

11. The freezing rain slapped him _____ in the face.

12. As babies get older, they _____ less on their parents.

13. If we _____ off in different directions, we have a better chance of finding our puppy.

14. The pressure is greater at the _____ than at the surface of the ocean.

Write two sentences using at least one of this lesson's vocabulary words in each.

15. _____

_____

16. _____

_____

Making Inferences

**Focus**

Readers **make inferences** about characters and events to understand a total picture in a story.

An **inference** is a statement a reader makes about a character or event from the story. To make an inference, the reader uses

- **information** from the story, such as examples, facts, reasons, and descriptions.
- **personal experience or knowledge,** such as memories and experiences the reader brings to the story.

Practice

Think of an event from "Who Eats What?" Write an inference about the event, such as why you think it happens or happened. Write the information from the story and the personal experience you used to make the inference.

Event: _____

_____

Inference: _____

_____

Information from the story: _____

_____

_____

Personal experience: _____

_____

Read the following paragraph. Then make an inference by answering the questions.

Harry's father and mother would be angry when they saw the table even though Harry had not meant to break it. He accidentally fell on the table while tossing a football in the house. Harry looked at the broken pieces scattered around the room. He knew the table could not be fixed.

1. What did Harry do? _____

_____

2. Is Harry worried? Why? _____

_____

3. Can Harry fix the table? Why? _____

_____

Apply Write a paragraph that continues the above story about Harry and the table. Include the inferences you made and add information that will let your readers make new inferences.

_____

_____

_____

_____

_____

Resource List

It is important to use several different sources to research your ideas, so you can cross-check information, or make sure it is correct. Different sources can also give you different types of information. This will provide you with a broader picture of your topic.

Look over the list of resources, and place a checkmark by each resource you have used or plan to use when researching your topic.

☐ encyclopedias   ☐ magazines and newspapers

☐ atlas   ☐ the Internet

☐ books

Answer the following questions about resources.

1. Which resource would give you the most recent information on a topic?

_____

2. Where is the best place to look for maps to aid your research?

_____

3. Some resources are less reliable than others. Which resource should you be most cautious about when using it for research?

_____

4. Why might this resource be less than reliable at times?

_____

_____

5. If you want some basic, general information on a broad topic, where might you look?

_____

Resource List

People and places are other resources that can be very helpful to you as you conduct your research. Interviewing people and visiting places can bring a unique perspective to your topic.

6. Who will you interview about your topic?

_____

7. What questions will you ask this person?

_____

_____

_____

8. What are some places you could visit to help you research your topic?

_____

9. Choose a place to visit. What will you do while you're there?

_____

_____

10. Think of a creative way to use what you've learned from people and places in your research presentation. What might you do to enhance your project?

_____

_____

_____

Writing: Writing Research Reports

Think   **Audience: Who** is going to read your report?

_____

Purpose: What is the reason for writing this report?

_____

Prewriting   **A research report helps you form a question about an issue you find interesting, gather information about it from various sources, and answer the question based on your findings.**

Use the following organizer to plan your report.

My question: _____

_____

Sources I will use to answer my question: _____

_____

Possible answers to my question: _____

_____

Notes: _____

_____

Revising Use this checklist to revise your research report.

☐ Are the main points in your report presented in logical order?

☐ Does your introduction grab your readers' attention?

☐ Did you answer the question with support from various sources?

Editing Use this checklist to correct mistakes. Use proofreader's marks as you read your first draft.

☐ Make sure that all words are spelled correctly.

☐ Check all punctuation to make sure that it is correct.

☐ Make sure that sentences and proper nouns begin with capital letters.

Publishing Use this checklist to get ready for publication.

☐ Write or type a neat final copy.

☐ Read your work one more time. Correct any errors.

☐ Share your report with your class or a group of younger students.

☐ Include a diagram, photograph, or other illustration to help readers understand your topic.

☐ Give an oral presentation of your research report to your class. Use illustrations, charts, diagrams, or tables in your presentation.

☐ Consider publishing your research report in the school newspaper or a community newsletter.

Prefix *re-* and Homographs

Focus

- A **prefix** is one or more letters added to the beginning of a root or base word that changes the word's meaning. Knowing the meaning of the prefix will help you figure out the meanings of unfamiliar words. The **prefix** *re-* means "again."

- For example, *reprogram* means "to program again."

- Remember that **homographs** are words that are spelled the same but have different meanings and different pronunciations.

- For example, the word *rest* has two meanings: "relax" and "the remainder."

Word List
1. bass
2. bow
3. close
4. conflict
5. converse
6. lead
7. object
8. putting
9. rearrange
10. recall
11. recover
12. re-create
13. refurnish
14. reinforce
15. relive
16. reoccurrence
17. resale
18. revise
19. rewire
20. rewrite

Challenge Words:
21. buffet
22. content
23. realign

Practice Write the homograph which best fits the meanings given.

1. tied on shoe, front of a ship

   _____

2. to be near, to shut _____

3. problem, disagreement _____

4. talk with, opposite idea _____

5. guiding, type of metal _____

6. an item, to oppose by speaking

   _____

7. to be happy, what is contained in something

   _____

8. a table of food, to repeatedly force

   _____

Use the meanings of the prefix and the base word to determine the meaning of the spelling word. Write the meaning of the spelling word on the line.

9. rewrite _____

10. refurnish _____

11. rearrange _____

12. revise _____

13. reoccurrence _____

14. resale _____

15. relive _____

16. rewire _____

17. re-create _____

18. realign _____

Apply **Write a sentence for each meaning of the homographs listed. Remember, there are at least two meanings for these words.**

19. putting

_____

_____

20. bass

_____

_____

Compound Subjects and Predicates

 **Focus**
- Every sentence has two parts—a subject and a predicate.
- A **simple subject** of a sentence is a noun that tells whom or what the sentence is about.
- A **compound subject** is two or more subjects that share the same predicate or predicates in a sentence. The verb in the sentence must agree in number with the subject.

  Example: *John and Erica* live in two different cities.

- A simple predicate of a sentence is a verb that tells what the subject does.

- A **compound predicate** is two or more predicates that refer to the same subject in a sentence.

  Example: The dog *walked* around the room and *sniffed* the furniture.

 **Practice** Write a sentence for each pair of bold-faced words, using the two words as a compound subject. The first one has been done for you.

1. Katie, teacher _____

_____

2. boy, dog _____

_____

3. carrots, potatoes _____

_____

4. table, chairs _____

_____

5. Lyle, Kyle _____

_____

6. My mom baked a turkey _____

_____

7. Lisa called Mary on the phone _____

_____

8. My cat played with her yarn _____

_____

9. The doctor checked my throat _____

_____

10. My dad fell asleep in his chair _____

_____

11. I emptied the trash _____

_____

Read this paragraph. Circle the complete subject in each sentence. Underline the complete predicate in each sentence. Write *CS* above any compound subjects and *CP* above any compound predicates.

David began to take tennis lessons. He learned how to hit

the ball and how to hold his racket. David and his brother

practiced for many hours each day. His coach told David that

he was ready for his first tennis tournament. David played

hard and served the ball well. He won the tournament.

Suffix *-ity*

 **Focus**
- Remember that a suffix is added to the end of a base word.
- The suffix *-ity* means "state or quality of being."

 **Practice** **Add the suffix *-ity* to the base words below to create a new word.**

1. personal _____

2. formal _____

3. national _____

4. uniform _____

5. curious _____

6. productive _____

7. regular _____

8. real _____

9. negative _____

10. prior _____

scarcity	quantity	possibility	responsibility
continuity	popularity	opportunity	similarity

11. His _____ showed when he took care of the cat for a week.

12. Having a chance to go to the White House to meet the president is a great

_____ .

13. The _____ of the bike became obvious when the store

sold out in two hours.

14. There was a large _____ of pencils on the teacher's desk at the beginning of the year.

15. The _____ between the real fruit and the plastic fruit is amazing.

16. The _____ of gasoline caused people to change their driving habits.

17. The _____ of rain tomorrow is ninety percent.

18. _____ is staying the same and being consistent throughout.

Selection Vocabulary

Focus

plump (plump) *adj.* having a full, rounded form (page 186)

shrivel (shri' vəl) *v.* to wrinkle and become small (page 186)

brittle (bri' təl) *adj.* easily broken (page 187)

decays (di kāz') *v.* form of **decay:** to slowly break down (page 187)

microbes (mī' krōbz) *n.* plural of **microbe:** a very tiny living thing; a microorganism (page 187)

swarming (swor' ming) *v.* form of **swarm:** to gather or live in a large group (page 188)

larva (lär' və) *n.* a young insect that hatches from an egg and has a wormlike form before growing into an adult (page 188)

burrow (bûr' ō) *n.* a hole in the ground to live in (page 189)

cocoons (kə künz') *n.* plural of **cocoon:** the silky envelope spun by the larvae of insects to protect themselves during a phase of growth (page 189)

enrich (en rich') *v.* to improve or make better by adding something (page 192)

circulate (sûr' kyə lāt) *v.* to flow freely (page 192)

teeming (tēm' ing) *v.* form of **teem:** to be full; to swarm (page 192)

Practice Write two sentences using at least one vocabulary word in each

1. _____

_____

2. _____

_____

Apply Circle the word in parentheses that best fits each sentence.

3. The bees were (swarming/shrivel) around a single flower.

4. What happens to a pumpkin after it (burrow/decays)?

5. Trent opened the windows so air could (enrich/circulate) through the house.

6. Many farmers (teeming / enrich) the soil by adding fertilizer.

7. When grapes (shrivel/decays), they become raisins.

8. My baby sister's (plump / brittle) cheeks are adorable.

9. Try not to hurt that butterfly. Its wings are very (brittle / circulate).

10. The mole hid in its (burrow/microbes).

Write a short paragraph that contains three or more of the selection vocabulary words

_____

_____

_____

_____

Fact and Opinion

 **Focus**
Writers use **facts and opinions** to support ideas in their writing.
- A **fact** is a statement than can be proven true.

• An **opinion** is what someone feels or believes is true. Opinions cannot be proven true or false.

 **Practice**
Look through "What Rot! Nature's Mighty Recycler" for examples of facts and opinions. Write two facts and two opinions on the lines below.

1. Page: _____

Opinion: _____

_____

2. Page: _____

Fact: _____

_____

3. Page: _____

Opinion: _____

_____

4. Page: _____

Fact: _____

_____

Read the sentences below. In the spaces below, write *fact* if the sentence is a fact or *opinion* if it is an opinion.

5. _____ All German shepherd dogs are mammals.

6. _____ The success of a business depends on the age of its owners.

7. _____ Chicago is a city in the state of Illinois.

8. _____ The *Titanic* was a large ship that sank in the Atlantic Ocean.

9. _____ Being on an airplane is better than taking a train.

10. _____ Science is the most difficult subject.

11. _____ The space shuttle *Challenger* exploded shortly after takeoff.

12. _____ E.B. White is the best children's author.

13. _____ Fossil fuels are a limited resource.

14. _____ Sunsets are caused by the scattering of light in the atmosphere.

Apply

Write two sentences that are facts and two sentences that are opinions about the town or city in which you live.

15. _____

16. _____

_____

17. _____

_____

18. _____

_____

Diagrams

A diagram is an illustration of the parts of an object, an arrangement of objects, the steps in a process, or the stages in a cycle. Diagrams clarify written information in a book, magazine, or other resource by providing a picture to help readers see how things work.

Here are the kinds of information diagrams can show:

- how something is put together, such as roller skates
- how something is arranged, such as furniture in a room
- how something works, such as the hip or elbow joints in the body
- how to make something, such as a model airplane
- what steps make up a process, such as making steel
- what stages make up a cycle, such as the life cycle of a frog

Look at the diagram below.

Parts of an In-Line Skate

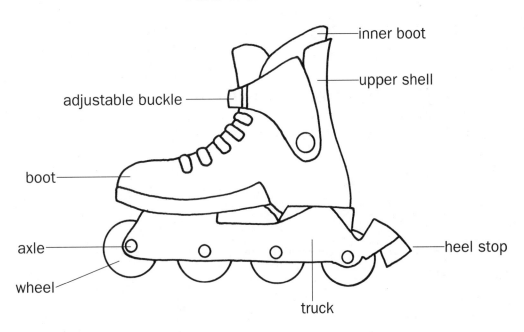

Diagrams

Notice the features of the diagram on page 111. These features are common to most diagrams.

- The **title** of a diagram tells what the diagram shows.
- **Labels** of a diagram tell about the parts of an object or the steps in a process.
- **Lines** lead from each label to a part of an object or one step in a process.
- **Arrows** show the order in which the steps of a process or the stages in a cycle take place. They may also show movement or direction.

Answer the following questions using the diagram of an in-line skate.

1. What parts of an in-line skate cover the foot and part of the leg?

   _____

   _____

2. Can you tell what the truck does by looking at the diagram? _____

   What does it do? _____

   _____

3. Which part helps you to stop rolling when you skate? _____

   Describe where that part is located on the skate. _____

   _____

   _____

Think of how you might use a diagram in your investigation. Write your ideas here.

_____

_____

Suffix -ity and Prefix in-

 **Focus**

- Remember **suffixes** are one or more letters added to the end of a root or base word. The spelling of the base word often changes when adding the suffix.

- The **suffix -ity** means "state or quality of being." For example, *humidity* refers to the state of being humid.

- A word with the suffix -ity is usually a noun.

- A **prefix** is one or more letters added to the beginning of a root or base word that changes the word's meaning. Knowing the meaning of the prefix will help you figure out the meanings of unfamiliar words. The **prefix in-** means "not" or "in."

- For example, *inexpensive* means "not expensive."

 **Practice**

Sort the spelling words into the categories of the prefix *in-* and suffix *-ity*.

Prefix *in-*

1. _____
2. _____
3. _____
4. _____
5. _____
6. _____
7. _____
8. _____
9. _____

Suffix *-ity*

10. _____
11. _____
12. _____
13. _____
14. _____
15. _____
16. _____
17. _____
18. _____
19. _____
20. _____

Word List

1. curiosity
2. identity
3. inadequate
4. inappropriate
5. inattention
6. incapable
7. inconclusive
8. incorporate
9. incredible
10. infinite
11. invaluable
12. opportunity
13. personality
14. possibility
15. productivity
16. quality
17. quantity
18. reality
19. responsibility
20. similarity

Challenge Words

21. indebted
22. indigenous
23. peculiarity

Circle the misspelled words in the sentence. Write the word with the correct spelling on the line.

21. It is inapropriate to talk with your mouth full. _____

22. That man's identitey was stolen. _____

23. The realitiey of the situation was unbelievable. _____

24. She was forever endebtid to him for his help. _____

25. The quaulitie of the dress was wonderful. _____

Apply Write the spelling word for each base word shown.

26. curious _____

27. similar _____

28. finite _____

29. capable _____

30. peculiar _____

31. possible _____

32. responsible _____

33. attention _____

34. credible _____

35. productive _____

36. adequate _____

37. conclusive _____

38. valuable _____

Coordinating Conjunctions

Focus

A **conjunction** is a word that connects words or groups of words. The words *and, but,* and *or* are **coordinating conjunctions.** They connect related words or groups of words.

Examples: You may mow the grass **or** help me wash the car.

Alex can help you, **but** she has other chores to do too.

Combine two simple sentences by adding a conjunction to form a **compound sentence.**

Example: Sally decided to rest. She wasn't really tired.

Sally decided to rest, **but** she wasn't really tired.

Practice

Combine each of these pairs of simple sentences to form a compound sentence using a coordinating conjunction.

1. We could play tennis. We could go swimming. _____

_____

2. Vince picked up the phone. He dialed the number. _____

_____

3. My teacher fell on the ice. He broke his arm. _____

_____

4. Mr. DeCarlo will get our mail. His wife will do it. _____

_____

Read the following draft. Then improve it by combining sentences to form compound sentences. Write your revision in the space provided.

Jillian bought a new kite. Tarah helped her put it together. Jillian tried it first. Tarah watched. Jillian said Tarah could try it. She wouldn't force her. Tarah decided to try it. She was successful. The kite flew high in the sky. The girls were excited. Their smiles soon turned to frowns. The kite was caught in a tree. Jillian went to get her dad. He got a ladder. He got the kite out of the tree.

_____

_____

_____

_____

_____

_____

_____

_____

_____

_____

Suffixes *-or* and *-less*

Practice   **Answer the questions that follow each given word.**

Protector

1. Identify the suffix and define it._____

_____

2. Study the base word and define it. _____

_____

3. Put the base word and suffix together to create a definition for the entire

word. _____

_____

restless

4. Identify the suffix, and define it. _____

_____

5. Study the base word, and define it. _____

_____

6. Put the base word and suffix together to create a definition for the entire

word. _____

_____

Apply Circle and define the suffix in each word.

7. oppressor _____

8. useless _____

9. hopeless _____

10. painless _____

Add the suffix -or or -less to each base word. Then write a definition for each new word.

11. govern _____

_____

12. thought _____

_____

13. vend _____

_____

14. instruct _____

_____

15. fault _____

_____

Selection Vocabulary

 **Focus**

squawking (skwok' ing) *v.* form of **squawk:** to utter a harsh, abrupt scream (page 202)

generations (je nə rā' shənz) *n.* plural of **generation:** a group of people born around the same time (page 202)

ancestors (an' ses' tûrz) *n.* plural of **ancestor:** someone from long ago who is in a direct relation to you; for example, a great-great-grandparent (page 202)

pollinate (po' lə nāt') *v.* to spread pollen from flower to flower, allowing fruit and seeds to grow (page 204)

wither (wi' <u>th</u>ûr) *v.* to dry up; to shrivel (page 204)

smoldering (smōl' dûr ing) *v.* form of **smolder:** to burn and smoke without flames (page 204)

ruins (rōō' ənz) *n.* plural of **ruin:** the remains of something destroyed or decayed (page 204)

oxygen (ok' si jən) *n.* a gas that makes up about one-fifth of Earth's atmosphere and that animals must breathe to live (page 206)

clinging (kling' ing) *v.* form of **cling:** to hold on tightly (page 208)

murmured (mûr' mərd) *v.* past tense of **murmur:** to make a low, soft sound (page 208)

dangle (dang' gəl) *v.* to hang; to swing loosely (page 212)

suspended (sə spen' dəd) *v.* past tense of **suspend:** to hang (page 212)

 **Practice**

Write *T* in the blank if the sentence for the vocabulary word is correct. Write *F* if the sentence is false. For each *F* answer, write the word that fits the definition.

1. If something is *smoldering,* it is holding on tight. ____ _____

2. *Generations* are the remains of something destroyed. ____ _____

3. Animals must breathe *oxygen* to live. ____ _____

4. *Pollinate* means "spread pollen from flower to flower." ____ _____

5. Your great-grandparents are your *ancestors.* ____ _____

6. If something is *clinging,* it is burning or smoking without flames.

____ _____

7. *Dangle* means "to dry up and shrivel." ____ _____

 **Write the word that best fits each clue below.**

8. This is a gas that is in the air we breathe. What is it?

_____

9. These people are relatives of yours who lived long ago.

Who are they? _____

10. The baby monkey was hanging on to its mother tightly.

What was he doing? _____

11. When bees do this to flowers, it helps fruit and seeds to grow.

What is it? _____

12. If your front baby teeth hang by a thread before you pull them out,

what do they do? _____

13. The wind made a low, soft sound outside my window. What did it do?

_____

14. A forest is doing this when there is smoke without flames.

What is it? _____

15. When flowers dry up, we say they do this. What is it?

_____

16. Thirty years typically separate each of these in your family.

What are they? _____

Classify and Categorize

**Focus**   Good readers classify items into categories as they read to help them organize information and understand what they read.

   Classifying means arranging people, animals, or things into different groups or **categories.** When classifying people, ideas, places, or things

- name the categories, or groups, for similar items.
- list items that fit the category.

Animals ◄—— *Category*
Bats
Lizards
Mice
Fish
Turtles

Some items can fit more than one category.

Animals	**Reptiles**
Turtles	Turtles
Lizards	Lizards

Practice   **Look through "The Great Kapok Tree" and list all the items that fit the categories below.**

1. Rainforest animals: _____

_____

2. Birds: _____

_____

3. Mammals: _____

_____

Apply Look at the items in the box below. List each item from the box under the correct category. Remember that some items can fit into more than one category.

Items			
notebook	fruit	juice	sandwich
stamps	paper	pen	

Things for Lunch

_____

_____

_____

School Supplies

_____

_____

_____

Things for Writing and Mailing Letters

_____

_____

_____

Whales have characteristics that make them different from other types of sea creatures. For instance, whales are mammals. Think of other types of animals, such as reptiles or birds. Name and write this new category for a type of animal. Then, list any animals that fit this category in the spaces below.

_____

_____

_____

_____

_____

Using Visual Aids

Charts, graphs and tables are visual presentations of information. Use them to present a lot of information in a small amount of space.

- There are many types of charts, tables and graphs. The following is an example of a **chart.** Charts contain rows and columns. Each row and column tells what type of information is in the chart.

- A **pie chart** is a circle that breaks things down into parts of a whole.

Which foods do the birds like best?

	Suet	Millet	Peanut Hearts	Thistle	Cracked Corn
Blue Jay	x		x		
Finch	x			x	
Grosbeak	x				
Dove	x	x	x		x

- A **bar graph** compares things or shows how something has changed.

What's in that Birdbrain Deluxe birdfood mixture?

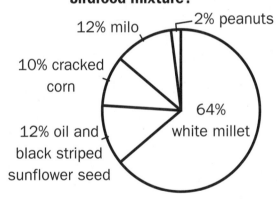

Percentage of Schools with Internet Access

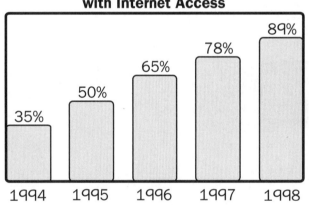

Use the birdfeeding chart to answer these questions.

1. Which birds like to eat millet? _____

2. What do finches like to eat? _____

3. What food do all the birds eat? _____

Using Visual Aids

Read the paragraph below. Turn the information into a chart or graph and give it a title.

This is information about major earthquakes in the United States in the 20th century. There was an earthquake in San Francisco, California, on April 18, 1906. It measured 7.7 on the Richter scale and caused 700 deaths. An earthquake in Prince William Sound, Alaska, on March 27, 1964, measured 9.2 on the Richter scale and caused 130 deaths. An earthquake in Yucca Valley, California, on June 28, 1992, measured 7.6 and caused one death.

Persuasive Writing

 **Think** **Audience: Who** will read your persuasive report?

_____

Purpose: What do you want your readers to think about your report?

_____

Prewriting Use this graphic organizer to plan your persuasive report. Write your opinion in the middle circle. Then write your supporting facts on the lines.
Think about how you want to present your facts. You might choose to start with your strongest point or build up to it and state it last.

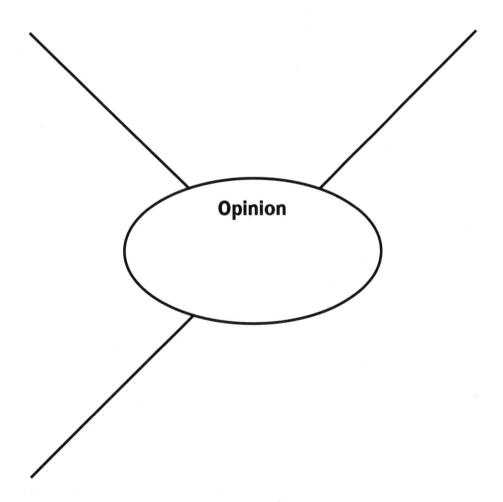

Revising — Use this checklist to revise your description.

☐ Has the purpose you chose during prewriting been met?

☐ Did you clearly state your opinion?

☐ Did you include facts that support your opinion?

☐ Did you begin in a way that will grab your audience's attention?

☐ Will readers be able to tell that the topic is important to you?

☐ Did you organize your facts in a logical order?

Editing — Use this checklist to correct mistakes in your revised draft. Do not let your readers be distracted by mistakes.

☐ Did you check your spelling and punctuation?

☐ Did you capitalize proper nouns and the first word in each sentence?

☐ Did you write in complete sentences, avoiding fragment, run-on, rambling, and awkward sentences?

Publishing — Use this checklist to get ready for publication.

☐ Write or type a neat final copy.

☐ Include a drawing or a photograph with your report.

☐ Share your persuasive report with others.

☐ If possible, use multimedia sources to help publish your report.

Greek Root *Path* and Suffix *-or*

Focus

- Many English words have Greek roots. When you know the meaning of these roots, you can figure out many unfamiliar English words.

- The **Greek root** *path* can mean "feeling" or "disease."

- Remember that **suffixes** are one or more letters added to the end of a root or base word. The spelling of the base word often changes when adding the suffix.

- The **suffix *-or*** means "someone who" or "something that." For example, an *actor* refers to someone who acts.

- Adding the suffix *-or* usually changes verbs to nouns.

Practice

Based on your knowledge of English words that come from Greek roots, write a definition for the following words. Refer to a dictionary if necessary.

1. apathy _____

2. telepathy _____

3. empathy _____

4. pathetic _____

5. sympathy _____

6. pathogen _____

7. pathos _____

8. homeopathy _____

Word List

1. ancestor
2. animator
3. apathy
4. auditor
5. contributor
6. creditor
7. debtor
8. director
9. editor
10. elevator
11. empathy
12. governor
13. pathetic
14. sailor
15. successor
16. sympathy
17. telepathy
18. traitor
19. vendor
20. visitor

Challenge Words

21. homeopathy
22. pathogen
23. pathos

Write the base word for each spelling word given.

9. visitor _____

10. animator _____

11. vendor _____

12. auditor _____

13. traitor _____

14. contributor _____

15. successor _____

16. creditor _____

17. sailor _____

18. debtor _____

19. governor _____

20. director _____

21. elevator _____

22. editor _____

Apply **Create a sentence for each word listed.**

23. contributor _____

_____

24. pathogen _____

_____

25. successor _____

_____

26. apathy _____

_____

Run-Ons and Sentence Fragments

**Focus**
- A complete sentence must have a subject and a predicate. A complete sentence expresses a complete thought.

Example: Harry's new puppy did not eat its food.

- A **sentence fragment** is a group of words that does not express a complete thought. A sentence fragment is missing a subject, a predicate, or both; for example: Harry's new puppy. Did not eat its food.

- A sentence with no punctuation or coordinating conjunctions between two or more complete sentences is a **run-on** sentence. For example: The puppy has been quiet all day Harry does not know whether it is sick or not.

**Practice**   **The following sentence fragments are missing either a subject or predicate. Rewrite each sentence fragment as a complete sentence.**

1. Everyone in the whole town. _____

_____

2. Took the stick away from her. _____

_____

3. The angry baseball player. _____

_____

4. Sat on his bed for a long time. _____

_____

5. Asked his brother for a favor. _____

_____

6. The funny clown. _____

_____

7. Leaves Monday. _____

_____

8. All the fishermen. _____

Apply Rewrite the following paragraph. Correct the run-on sentences by using a coordinating conjunction or separating it into two sentences.

Michaela loves to draw horses she is a talented artist. She owns a horse at her farm its name is Cocheece. She has daily chores to take care of Cocheece they include cleaning the stall, brushing his hair and mane and feeding him. After her homework and chores are done Michaela takes Cocheece on a long ride through the pasture and up the hills then along the driveway back to the stable. Michaela loves Cocheece.

_____

_____

_____

_____

_____

_____

_____

Multiple-Meaning Words and Prefix *co-*

Focus
- **Multiple-Meaning Words** are words that have several meanings depending on how they are used in a sentence.
- The prefix *co-* means "with" or "together." The prefix may be connected to the base word with a hyphen.

Practice Decide which meaning of the underlined word best fits the context of the sentence. Circle the correct answer.

1. Josh needed a new <u>bat</u> and glove to improve his game.

   a winged mammal   a wooden club   to strike or hit

2. She panicked as she began to <u>sink</u> in the quicksand.

   to become submerged   a place for washing dishes

3. Please arrange the note cards in alphabetical <u>order</u>.

   a food request   organization   a command

Choose a word with the prefix *co-* from the word box to complete each sentence below.

cooperate	coworkers	coexist	coordinated	cohost

4. Athletes are more _____ than most people.

5. Many different animals _____ in a single ecosystem.

Write the meaning of the underlined word in each sentence on the first line. Then provide another meaning of the word on the second line.

6. Do you think this tape will <u>stick</u> to the wall?

_____   _____

7. Tim waited all day for the phone to <u>ring</u>.

_____   _____

8. She lost her <u>pen</u>, so she could not finish her letter.

_____   _____

9. That dog's <u>bark</u> is worse than its bite.

_____   _____

10. What <u>kind</u> of movies do you like?

_____   _____

Add the prefix *co-* to the base words below, and define the word that is formed.

11. discover _____   _____

12. produce _____   _____

13. resident _____   _____

14. signer _____   _____

_____

15. star _____   _____

_____

Selection Vocabulary

**Focus**

domain (dō mān') *n.* a territory governed by a single ruler (page 232)

peninsula (pə nin' sə le) *n.* an area of land that juts out from a larger area of land and is surrounded by water on three sides (page 232)

submerged (səb mûrjd') *v.* past tense of **submerge:** to cover or overflow with water (page 232)

isolated (ī' sə lāt' əd) *v.* past tense of **isolate:** to set apart or cut off from others (page 232)

fossilized (fä' sə līzd) *v.* past tense of **fossilize:** to become preserved and hardened in rock (page 233)

paleontologists (pā' lē ən tol' ə jists) *n.* plural of **paleontologist:** a person who studies fossils (page 233)

mortar (môr' tər) *n.* a material used to bind together bricks or stones (page 234)

presidios (pri si' dē ōs') *n.* plural of presidio: a fort or military post (page 236)

missionaries (mish' ə ner' ēz) *n.* plural of **missionary:** a person who is sent to teach and spread a particular religion (page 236)

epidemics (ep' i dem' iks) *n.* plural of **epidemic:** an outbreak of a contagious disease (page 238)

dispute (dis pūt') *n.* an argument or conflict (page 239)

ceded (sēd' əd) *v.* past tense of **cede:** to surrender possession of (page 239)

**Practice**   Fill in each blank with a vocabulary word from this lesson that best completes each sentence.

1. The builder ordered bricks and _____ to repair the chimney.

2. The best way to solve a _____ is with words instead of violence.

3. After being _____ on an island alone for five days, I was relieved to see my family.

4. During the excavation, a group of _____ discovered a rare fossil that was more than five million years old.

5. I _____ my feet in the pool to cool off after a long day in the sun.

6. The state of Florida is an example of a _____.

mortar	ceded	isolated
presidios	fossilized	dispute
domain	missionaries	epidemics

7. _____ forts or military posts

8. _____ a territory governed by a single ruler

9. _____ outbreaks of a contagious disease

10. _____ an argument or conflict

11. _____ surrendered possession of

12. _____ people who spread a particular religion

13. _____ a material used to bind together bricks or stones

14. _____ became preserved and hardened in rock

15. _____ set apart or cut off from others

Compare and Contrast

Focus To compare means telling how things are alike. To contrast means telling how things are different.

- To **compare** means telling how two or more things are alike. For example: A triangle and a square are alike. They are both shapes.

- To **contrast** means telling how two or more things are different. For example: A triangle and a square are different. A triangle has three sides. A square has four sides.

Practice Look at the pairs of words below. Write how they are alike in the spaces below.

1. carrot   corn _____

2. trumpet   guitar _____

3. car   bicycle _____

4. cat   dog _____

Look at the pairs of words. Write how they are different in the spaces below.

5. carrot   corn _____

6. trumpet   guitar _____

7. car   bicycle _____

8. cat   dog _____

Look at the pairs of words in the chart below. Write in the chart how the words are alike and how they are different.

Words	Alike	Different
chicken rabbit		
tree flower		
baseball basketball		
fiction nonfiction		
pencil marker		

Apply Think about two things that you might compare and contrast. Write the pair of things in the first column of the chart below. In the second column, write how they are alike. Write how they are different in the third column.

Words	Alike	Different

Comprehension Skill • *Skills Practice 1*

Using Time Lines

A **time line** can help you understand when important events occurred and the order in which they happened. A time line may cover any length of time, from the lifetime of a person to a historical period of hundreds or thousands of years.

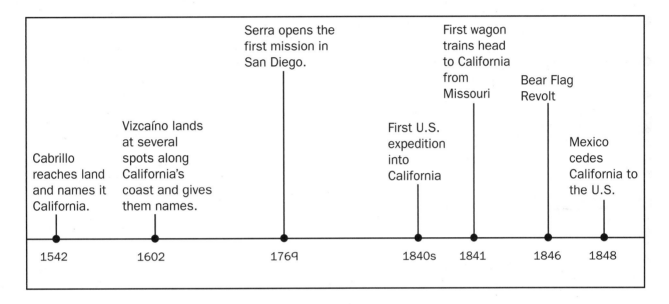

		Serra opens the first mission in San Diego.		First wagon trains head to California from Missouri	Bear Flag Revolt	
	Vizcaíno lands at several spots along California's coast and gives them names.		First U.S. expedition into California			Mexico cedes California to the U.S.
Cabrillo reaches land and names it California.						
1542	1602	1769	1840s	1841	1846	1848

Here are some things to remember about time lines.

- Each dot on the line represents a date.

- Each dot represents at least one event.

- A time line usually has a title that indicates the type of information that is shown on the line.

- Events are listed on the time line from left to right in the order of occurrence. The earliest event appears at the far left.

- A time line can be made for any set of events. However, time lines usually show meaningful relationships between events.

- Record only important events on a time line. Avoid minor details and unimportant events.

- You could use two time lines to compare and contrast when different events occur.

- Time lines are effective in quickly providing readers with the main ideas of your writing.

Using Time Lines (continued)

What important school events have happened since the first day of school? Make a time line of these events from the first day of school to today. Begin by listing four important events and the dates of these events in the spaces below. Then put the dates and a brief description of each event on the time line in the box.

1. _____

2. _____

3. _____

4. _____

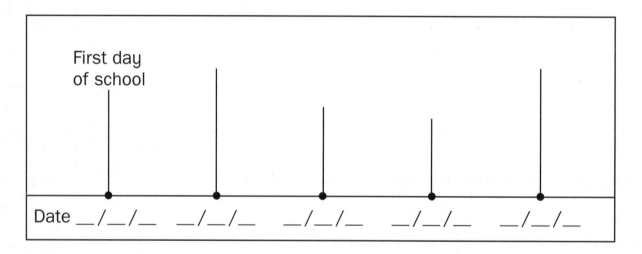

How might you use a time line during your investigation?

_____

_____

_____

_____

_____

_____

_____

Inquiry • *Skills Practice 1*

Writing: Persuasive Writing–Focus on Main Idea and Details

Think   **Audience: Who** will read your persuasive piece?

_____

Purpose: What do you want your readers to understand about your writing?

_____

Prewriting   Use this chart to assist you when you are writing your main topic idea in this piece. Pretend that you are one of the first explorers to reach California—just like the explorers in "The First Californians." You have to persuade your crew to go with you to explore the unknown land of California.

In one column, list the main reasons for exploration. Support each idea with specific ideas or examples. In the other column, list the opposite view of each idea you have listed in the first column. Again, provide support.

Revising

Use this checklist to revise your persuasive writing.

☐ Has the purpose you chose during prewriting been met?

☐ Did you clearly state your opinion?

☐ Did you include facts that support your opinion?

☐ Did you begin in a way that will grab your audience's attention?

☐ Will your readers be able to tell that the topic is important to you?

Editing

Use this checklist to correct mistakes. Use proofreader's marks as you read your first draft.

☐ Make sure that all words are spelled correctly.

☐ Check all punctuation to make sure that it is correct.

☐ Make sure that sentences and proper nouns begin with capital letters.

☐ Did you write in complete sentences and with no fragment or run-on sentences?

Publishing

Use this checklist to get ready for publication.

☐ Write or type a neat final copy.

☐ Read your work one more time. Correct any errors.

☐ Even if you used a computer spell-checking program on your work, check for misspellings.

☐ You may wish to include a photograph or a photocopy of a picture of the object with your description.

Multiple-Meaning Words and Prefix co-

Focus

- Remember that a **multiple-meaning word** has different meanings depending on how it is used in a sentence. The spelling of the word does not change.

- Remember that the **prefix co-** means "together" or "with." It is sometimes attached to a base word with a hyphen. It does not affect a word's part of speech.

Practice Sort the Word List spelling words under the correct heading.

Multiple-meaning words

1. _____
2. _____
3. _____
4. _____
5. _____
6. _____
7. _____
8. _____
9. _____
10. _____
11. _____
12. _____
13. _____

Prefix co-

14. _____
15. _____
16. _____
17. _____
18. _____
19. _____
20. _____

Word List

1. account
2. bank
3. club
4. coagulate
5. coaxial
6. coextensive
7. cofounder
8. cohost
9. cooperate
10. copilot
11. fine
12. fluke
13. lumber
14. pupil
15. right
16. rose
17. snap
18. stalk
19. tail
20. trunk

Challenge Words

21. coefficient
22. coincidence
23. coordinate

Write the spelling word next to its meaning. Some words may be used twice.

21. _____ a student

22. _____ went higher

23. _____ the sloped land along a river

24. _____ wood used for building

25. _____ the rear compartment of a car

26. _____ of high quality

27. _____ part of the eye

28. _____ very thin

29. _____ correct

30. _____ part of an elephant

Write the spelling word that is formed from each base word below.

31. extend _____

32. operate _____

33. found _____

34. pilot _____

35. host _____

Prepositions

Focus

Rule	Example
• A **preposition** is a word that relates a noun, pronoun, or group of words to some other word in the sentence. Prepositions usually indicate relationships of time or place.	• The cookies are **on** the third shelf. They are stacked **above** the crackers.
• The noun or pronoun that follows a preposition in a sentence is called the **object of the preposition.** A preposition must have an object. It can't stand alone.	• The box of spaghetti is **beneath** the **crackers.** (*Crackers* is the object of the preposition *beneath.*) The sauce should be **beside** the **spaghetti.** (*Spaghetti* is the object of the preposition *beside.*)
• A **prepositional phrase** is made up of a preposition, its object, and any words in between.	• The food is **in the cabinet.** The cabinet is **near the window.**

Practice   **Read the paragraph. Circle all of the prepositions.**

Mongolia is a country on the continent of Asia. It is above China and below Russia. The capital city is near a river. Ulan Bator, the capital city, is one of the largest cities in Mongolia. There are several large cities throughout China and Russia. Have you ever traveled around China and Russia?

Read the paragraph. Circle all of the prepositions. Write the word
***object* above the object of the preposition.**

Many people travel across North America in cars. The United States is
between Canada and Mexico. The Rio Grande River runs along the American
border with Mexico, but people can still drive to that country. Several of the
Great Lakes are also near our border with Canada, but visitors can drive across
them by using a bridge. Families sometimes visit Canada or Mexico during a
vacation.

 **Apply** **Read the paragraph. Circle all of the prepositions.**
Draw an *X* through each object of a preposition.
Underline each prepositional phrase.

People live in many different areas throughout the United States. Some live
with animals on a farm. Others may live in an apartment in a big city. Another
group might live near the water, and many children live on quiet streets in small
towns. Considering the laws of our country, Americans can choose where they
want to live.

Suffix *-er* and Latin Root *nat*

• The suffix **-er** means "one who." When added to a verb, the word usually becomes a noun.

• The Latin root **nat** means "born."

Add the suffix **-er** to the words below to make a new word. Then define the new word that is formed.

1. paint _____   _____

2. dance _____   _____

3. interpret _____   _____

4. plan _____   _____

Look at the words *prenatal* and *unnatural*.

5. What is the root in *prenatal*?

_____

6. What does this root mean?

_____

7. What does the entire word mean?

_____

8. Name another word that contains this root.

_____

9. Use your word in a sentence.

_____

10. Based on your knowledge of the Latin root *nat*, what do you think

unnatural means? _____

**Apply**   **Think of a word with the suffix -er to fill in the blanks in the sentences below.**

11. The _____ needs the blueprints to start construction on the house.

12. Where did the _____ get lost on his walk through the woods?

13. I was the _____ with the fastest time in the race.

14. Would you say you are more of a _____ or a follower?

15. The _____ wrote the day's assignment on the chalkboard.

16. I had an opportunity to hear the _____ discuss his novel.

17. The _____ located in Paris, is a famous sculpture depicting a man deep in thought.

18. To become an Olympic _____ you would have to spend years on the slopes.

Use the words from the word box to complete the sentences below.

natives	innate	nature	natural

19. Walking through the forest makes you appreciate the beauty of

_____ .

20. The _____ on the island do not like having foreigners bother them.

21. I would rather have organic food with _____ ingredients.

22. His _____ love for animals was probably inherited from his father.

Selection Vocabulary

Focus

rumors (rōō' mûrz) *n.* plural of **rumor:** a story without proof that passes from person to person (page 248)

trapper (trap' pər) *n.* a person whose business is the trapping of animals for their furs (page 249)

distract (di strakt') *v.* to draw attention away from what someone is doing (page 249)

deserted (di zûr' təd) *v.* past tense of **desert:** to leave; to abandon (page 250)

roamed (rōmd) *v.* past tense of **roam:** to go from place to place without purpose or direction (page 250)

impressed (im prest') *v.* past tense of **impress:** to have a strong effect on the mind or feelings (page 251)

territory (târ' ə tor' ē) *n.* an area of land owned by a country, but whose people do not have the rights of that country (page 251)

abundance (ə bun' dunts) *n.* a large amount (page 251)

elegant (e' li gənt) *adj.* rich and fine in quality (page 253)

hardships (härd' ships') *n.* plural of **hardship:** something that causes difficulty, pain, or suffering (page 253)

typical (ti' pi kəl) *adj.* average; normal for its kind (page 254)

canteens (kan tēnz') *n.* plural of **canteen:** a small metal container for carrying water to drink (page 254)

Practice **Circle the word in parentheses that best fits each sentence.**

1. It was a(n) (abundance/typical) day at school, until something strange happened.

2. The lost puppy (roamed/deserted) the streets for three days until someone rescued it and found its owner.

3. We filled our (hardships/canteens) with water before beginning our eight-mile hike through the woods.

4. Jaime tried to ignore the (rumors/canteens) because he knew they were not true.

5. The (territory/elegant) dining room had expensive silk napkins and the most beautiful fine china I had ever seen.

6. The town was (impressed/deserted) years ago, and now all that remains are a few rundown buildings.

Apply Match each word on the left to its definition on the right.

7. trapper

a. rich and fine in quality

8. hardships

b. went from place to place without purpose

9. impressed

c. to draw attention away from what someone is doing

10. distract

d. having no people

11. abundance

e. a person who catches animals for their fur

12. territory

f. stories without proof that pass from person to person

13. canteens

g. had a strong effect on the mind or feelings

14. deserted

h. small containers for carrying water

15. rumors

i. a large amount

16. typical

j. average; normal

17. roamed

k. things that cause difficulty, pain, or suffering

18. elegant

l. an area of land owned by a country

Printed Resources

Find magazines, newspapers, or other printed resources (such as a newsletter) that have information about the topic you chose for your investigation. Choose three different resources that are about the same topic, such as doctors' opinions about herbal medicine. Write the title of the resource, the title of the article, and the date of the publication. Then, write a brief summary of each article.

1. Resource title: _____

Title of article: _____

Date: _____

Summary: _____

_____

_____

_____

2. Resource title: _____

Title of article: _____   Date: _____

Summary: _____

_____

_____

3. Resource title: _____

Title of article: _____   Date: _____

Summary: _____

_____

Write two paragraphs based on the summaries you wrote. Make sure your paragraphs cover the main topic of the articles you selected. Remember to answer the questions *who, what, where, when,* and *why* as you write about the topic. Write an interesting title for your paragraphs.

Title: _____

_____

_____

_____

_____

_____

_____

_____

_____

_____

_____

_____

_____

_____

_____

_____

_____

_____

Writing: Personal Narrative

 **Audience: Who** is going to read your narrative?

_____

Purpose: What is the reason for writing this narrative?

_____

 **A cluster web is a great way to visually organize your ideas, starting with your main idea and expanding your ideas from there. Use the cluster web below to help you organize your thoughts for your personal narrative.**

Write your memorable event in the middle. Then fill in any details about your experience that you would like to include in your narrative.

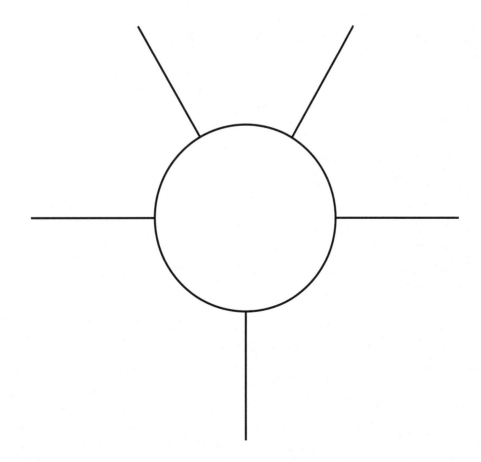

Revising

Use this checklist to revise your personal narrative.

☐ Is it clear to readers why this event is memorable to you and what you learned from it?

☐ Did you use concrete sensory details to describe your thoughts and feelings?

☐ Does your opening sentence/paragraph grab your readers' attention?

☐ Did you provide enough context for the reader to imagine the world of the event or experience?

Editing

Use this checklist to correct mistakes. Use proofreader's marks as you read your first draft.

☐ Are all the words in your narrative spelled correctly?

☐ Did you use correct end punctuation?

☐ Have you corrected any missing words, fragments or run-on sentences?

Publishing

Use this checklist to get ready for publication.

☐ Give your personal narrative a memorable and meaningful title.

☐ Read your work one more time. Correct any errors.

☐ Write or type a neat final copy.

☐ Include illustrations or photographs. Present them neatly by pasting them onto a sheet of paper or by scanning and placing them in your electronic file.

☐ Send your narrative to a newspaper or magazine for possible publication. Make sure you have followed the publication's rules for preparing your writing for publication.

Suffix -er and Latin Root nat

Focus

- Remember that the suffix **-er** means "one who." When the suffix is added in this context it usually changes verbs to nouns.

- Remember that the suffix **-er** can also mean "more." It turns an adjective into its comparative form.

- When a word ends in a silent e, the e is dropped before adding -er, as in *later*. When a word ends in y, the y may change to i before adding -er, as in *scarier*. If the word ends in a consonant, the consonant may be doubled before adding -er, as in *hitter*.

- Remember that the **Latin root nat** means "born."

Practice Sort the Word List spelling words under the correct heading.

Word List

1. anatomy
2. astronomer
3. bearer
4. bigger
5. dancer
6. employer
7. flatter
8. flipper
9. gardener
10. harder
11. harvester
12. innate
13. miner
14. national
15. nature
16. painter
17. smaller
18. tastier
19. unnatural
20. worker

Challenge Words

21. cognate
22. greedier
23. naturalistic

Suffix -er meaning "one who"

1. _____
2. _____
3. _____
4. _____
5. _____
6. _____
7. _____
8. _____
9. _____
10. _____

Suffix -er meaning "more"

11. _____
12. _____
13. _____
14. _____
15. _____

Latin Root nat

16. _____
17. _____
18. _____
19. _____
20. _____

 **Apply** Write the words that have spelling changes when the suffix *-er* is added. Explain the spelling change.

21. _____   _____

22. _____   _____

23. _____   _____

24. _____   _____

25. _____   _____

26. _____   _____

Think of other non-selection vocabulary words that have spelling changes when the suffix -er is added. Write the word and what changes occurred.

_____

_____

_____

Divide the following words into their units of meaning.

	Prefix(es)	Root	Suffix(es)
27. innate	_____	_____	_____
28. national	_____	_____	_____
29. nature	_____	_____	_____
30. unnatural	_____	_____	_____

Adjectives and Prepositional Phrases

Focus   An **adjective** is a word that describes a noun or pronoun.

Remember: A **preposition** relates a noun, pronoun, or group of words to another word in the sentence. *(in, through, by, with)*

A **prepositional phrase** includes a preposition and its object. *(in the house)*

Sentences that are related can often be combined by putting some of the information into a prepositional phrase.

Example:
Many men built the railroad. John Henry was the hardest working man of them all.

New combined sentence:
Of the men who built the railroad, John Henry was the hardest working of them all.

Practice   **Circle all prepositional phrases in the following sentences.**

1. Mom said she could use some help around the house after the game.

2. My friend Stella had never heard of the Washington Redskins until today.

3. Watching football is my favorite pastime in the fall.

4. I enjoy watching the players run into the stadium from the locker room.

5. Why is that player standing behind everyone else?

6. Dad said he will take me to a game for my birthday in December.

7. We drove into the tunnel which passed through the mountain.

8. The stadium stood right by the ocean with many flags.

Combine these pairs of sentences into one sentence using a prepositional phrase.

9. Mark and Zack are brothers. Zack is the older one.

_____

10. I've traveled a lot of places. I liked Hawaii the best.

_____

11. I have read all of E. B. White's books. *Charlotte's Web* is my favorite.

_____

12. Holli and Monica enjoyed tonight's performance. They liked last night's

performance even better. _____

_____

Apply **Rewrite each of the following sentences as two separate sentences.**

13. Of all the subjects in school, math is my favorite. _____

_____

14. Of the six sports at my school, football has the most participants.

_____

_____

15. Of all the constellations in the sky, the easiest one to find is the Big Dipper.

_____

_____

16. Of all the states out west, I think Arizona is the one I would like to visit the most.

_____

_____

Suffixes *-sion* and *-tion* and Prefix *en-*

Focus
- The suffixes *-sion* and *-tion* mean "the act or process of" or "a state or condition of." It is often added to a verb, changing it into a noun. Remember that there may be spelling changes that occur when you are adding this suffix.
- The prefix *en-* means "into," "within," or "to cause to be."

Practice Choose the word that best fits each sentence. Circle your answer.

1. Our _____ about politics lasted several hours because we were passionate about the topic.
collection   persuasion   discussion

2. He gave a thorough _____ for how every part of the machine worked.
explanation   continuation   percussion

3. Without _____, farmers in dry areas would not be able to produce healthy crops.
infection   irrigation   dehydration

4. Who are you going to vote for in this year's _____?
election   examination   elevation

5. There are only three more weeks until our high school _____!
communication   graduation   contamination

 **Apply** Add the suffixes *-sion* or *-tion* to the words below to create a new word. Then define the word. Watch for spelling changes.

6. conclude _____

_____

7. vary _____

_____

8. tense _____

_____

9. isolate _____

_____

10. reject _____

_____

Think of three words with the prefix *en-*, and use each word in a sentence.

11. _____

_____

12. _____

_____

Word Analysis • *Skills Practice 1*

Selection Vocabulary

advance (ad vans') *v.* to move forward; to help the progress or growth of (page 264)

detained (di tānd') *v.* form of **detain:** to keep back; to delay (page 264)

omen (ō' mən) *n.* a sign of something that is going to happen (page 264)

vast (vast) *adj.* large; widespread (page 265)

scarce (skârs) *adj.* hard to find (page 268)

engaged (in gājd') *adj.* busy; occupied (page 268)

perilous (per' əl əs) *adj.* involving or full of great risk or harm (page 269)

emigrants (em' i grənts) *n.* plural of **emigrant:** a person who leaves his or her country to live in another country (page 270)

dilapidated (di lap' i dā' tĭd) *adj.* fallen into ruin or decay; broken down (page 270)

tremendous (tri men' dəs) *adj.* very large (page 274)

provisions (prə vi' zhənz) *n.* plural of **provision:** a supply of food and other necessary items (page 275)

climate (klĭ' mət) *n.* the average weather conditions of a place over a period of years (page 277)

 **Write the vocabulary word next to the group of words that have a similar meaning.**

1. broad; spacious; widespread   _____

2. run-down; damaged; decayed   _____

3. risky; dangerous; unsafe   _____

4. progress; go ahead; move on   _____

5. rare; limited; unusual   _____

6. supplies; equipment; food   _____

7. restrain; hold back; hinder   _____

8. Sarah and Kenyon left the United States to live in Australia. What are

   they? _____

9. I was so busy with my project that I lost track of time. What was I?

   _____

10. Different places on Earth have particular weather patterns. What do we

    call this? _____

11. What word explains why diamonds are so valuable?

    _____

12. The old building is about to collapse. What is it? _____

13. My flight was late, so I missed my meeting. What was I?

    _____

14. What do we call necessary items such as food and water?

    _____

15. While playing a board game, you land on "Move ahead two spaces."

    What are you supposed to do? _____

Map Skills

A map contains several elements that help the user find a variety of information including direction and distance. A map key explains specific features on a map. The compass rose displays the four directions: north, south, east, and west. And a map scale helps us determine distance on the ground.

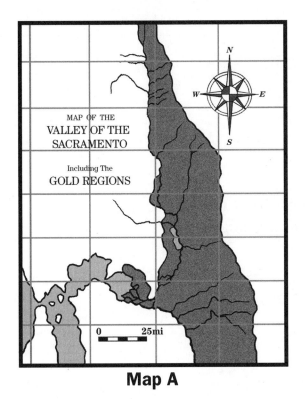

Map A

Map B

Identify the map key, the compass rose, and the map scale on these maps. Using a map of your town, locate streets and landmarks you know. Working with a partner, think of two places to travel to and from. Write directions for someone to follow to and from places in your town.

_____

_____

_____

_____

_____

Write five questions about either Map A or Map B. Give your questions to a classmate. When your classmate has finished answering them, discuss the questions. Share how maps could be useful in your research project for this or other units.

1. _____

2. _____

3. _____

4. _____

5. _____

Working with a partner, draw a map of an area (real or imaginary) that uses a map key, a compass rose, and a map scale.

Suffix -sion/tion and Prefix en-

Focus

- Remember that the suffix **-sion/-tion** means "the act or process of." It will change verbs to nouns with some irregular spelling changes.

- Remember that the prefix **en-** means "into," "within," or "to cause to be." This prefix does not change the spelling of the base word.

Practice Sort the Word List spelling words under the correct heading.

Suffix -sion

1. _____
2. _____
3. _____
4. _____

Suffix -tion

5. _____
6. _____
7. _____
8. _____

Prefix en-

9. _____
10. _____

11. _____
12. _____
13. _____
14. _____
15. _____
16. _____
17. _____
18. _____
19. _____
20. _____

Word List

1. collision
2. compulsion
3. corrosion
4. division
5. encircle
6. enclasp
7. encourage
8. endear
9. engrave
10. engross
11. enhance
12. enlarge
13. enliven
14. enrage
15. enrobe
16. entwine
17. relation
18. revolution
19. starvation
20. temptation

Challenge Words

21. commendation
22. digression
23. enthrone

Write the base word for the following words to visualize any spelling changes that occur. Use a dictionary if necessary.

21. collision _____

22. compulsion _____

23. corrosion _____

24. division _____

25. relation _____

26. revolution _____

27. starvation _____

28. temptation _____

Draw a line matching each word in the left column with its definition in the right column.

29. enrobe   **a.** to put confidence into

30. enrage   **b.** to cause to be bigger

31. encourage   **c.** to put into a twist

32. engrave   **d.** to put into clothes

33. entwine   **e.** to cause to be angry

34. enlarge   **f.** to hold in an embrace

35. enclasp   **g.** to carve into

Adverbs

Focus

- Remember that an **adjective** is a word that describes a noun or a pronoun.
- An **adverb** is a word that describes a verb, another adverb, or an adjective.
- Adverbs tell when, where, and to what extent an action is done.

Examples: Jill was sick **today.**   tells when

Sarah is **here** waiting for you.   tells where

The teacher is **always** on time.   tells to what extent

- Be careful when you use the terms *bad, badly, good,* and *well. Bad* and *good* are adjectives. *Badly* and *well* are adverbs.

Practice **Circle the adverbs in this paragraph.**

Scientists are working constantly to understand diseases. A disease can be relatively harmless, or it can be quite serious. There are thousands of diseases that can strike almost any part of the body. Some diseases are chronic, such as arthritis, which makes the joints swell painfully. Other diseases are caused by harmful bacteria that invade the body. Poor living conditions can also cause disease.

usually	often	also	about	typically	sometimes

Complete each sentence with an adverb from the words in the box.

The great white shark, _____ known as the white

pointer, is considered to be more dangerous to humans than any other shark. It

_____ lives in the open sea, but it _____

enters waters close to the shore. The white shark is known for its

_____ dangerous attacks on small boats. The shark

_____ grows to be _____ thirty-six feet long.

Apply **A word has been underlined in each sentence below. Write *Adj.* on the line if it is an adjective. Write *Adv.* if it is an adverb.**

1. _____ My goal is to earn <u>fifteen</u> dollars by the end of the day.

2. _____ I will have <u>Spanish</u> rice with my taco.

3. _____ If Ray is late <u>again</u>, he will miss the field trip.

4. _____ The <u>losing</u> team also receives a trophy.

5. _____ Everybody enjoys a <u>good</u> fictional book.

6. _____ Lucy studied <u>extremely</u> hard for the test.

Greek Roots *photo* and *hydr*

 **Focus** The Greek root **photo** means "light," and the Greek root **hydr** means "water."

Practice **Look at the words *photograph* and *dehydrate*.**

1. What are the roots in *photograph*? _____

2. What do the roots mean?

_____

3. Based on your knowledge of these roots, what do you think *photograph*

means? _____

4. Use *photograph* in a sentence.

_____

_____

5. What is the root in *dehydrate*? _____

6. What does this root mean? _____

7. If the prefix *de-* means "from" or "away," what do you think *dehydrate*

means? _____

8. Use dehydrate in a sentence.

_____

_____

List three words that contain the Greek root *photo,* and write their meanings. Use a dictionary, if necessary.

9. _____

_____

10. _____

11. _____

List three words that contain the Greek root *hydr,* and write their meanings. Use a dictionary, if necessary.

12. _____

13. _____

_____

14. _____

Use one of your words from each root in a sentence.

15. _____

16. _____

Write a brief paragraph using two words with the Greek root *photo* and one with the Greek root *hydr.*

_____

_____

_____

_____

_____

Selection Vocabulary

Focus

prominent (prom' ə nənt) *adj.* leading; important; well-known (page 286)

timbers (tim' bərz) *n.* plural of **timber:** a piece of wood forming part of a structure (page 288)

daggers (dag' ərz) *n.* plural of **dagger:** a short swordlike weapon with a pointed blade and a handle (page 289)

stampede (stam pēd') *v.* to flee in panic (page 290)

debris (də • brē') *n.* the remains of anything broken down or destroyed (page 290)

hoarse (hôrs) *adj.* having a weak or rough voice, often as a result of shouting (page 292)

rubble (ru' bəl) *n.* the remains of something that has been destroyed or broken (page 292)

scrabble (skra' bəl) *v.* to scratch or dig frantically with the hands (page 292)

aftershock (af' tər shäk') *n.* a small earthquake or tremor that follows a major earthquake (page 293)

cisterns (sis' tərnz) *n.* plural of **cistern:** a tank or container for storing or holding water (page 294)

eerie (ēr' ē) *adj.* strange and frightening (page 297)

billowing (bil' ō ing) *v.* form of **billow:** to rise up in a large surging mass (page 297)

Practice

Write the vocabulary word that best matches the underlined word or phrase in the sentences below.

1. The building was demolished and the <u>remaining pile of broken pieces</u> was

hauled away. _____

2. There are still a few underground <u>containers for storing water</u> that the city

still uses. _____

3. The museum had an entire exhibit dedicated to ancient <u>swordlike weapons</u>

from all parts of the world. _____

4. The workers cleaned up the <u>remains</u> of the home after the tornado.

_____

5. My voice was <u>scratchy and weak</u> after shouting at the football game for

three hours. _____

timbers	eerie	billowing	stampede
aftershock	scrabble	prominent	

6. _____ to scratch frantically with the hands

7. _____ rising in a large surging mass

8. _____ to flee in panic

9. _____ a small tremor that follows a major earthquake

10. _____ pieces of wood that form part of a structure

11. _____ strange and frightening

12. _____ important or well-known

Write six sentences using at least one of this lesson's vocabulary words in each.

13. _____

_____

14. _____

_____

15. _____

_____

16. _____

_____

17. _____

_____

18. _____

_____

Drawing Conclusions

 Focus   Writers provide information in a story to help readers draw conclusions about characters and story events.

Drawing conclusions means taking small pieces of information about a character or story event and using them to make a statement about that character or event.

The **conclusion** may not be stated in the text but should be supported by details in the text.

Practice   **Look through "The Earth Dragon Awakes." Choose a character or story event and draw a conclusion about it. Write the character's name or the story event. Then, write your conclusion, three sentences from the story with details that support your conclusion, and the page numbers where the sentences are found.**

Character or story event: _____

Page: _____ Sentence with details: _____

_____

_____

Page: _____ Sentence with details: _____

_____

Conclusion: _____

Page: _____ Sentence with details: _____

_____

Conclusion: _____

_____

Read the paragraph and then draw a conclusion. Write the sentences from the paragraph that have details which support your conclusion.

The thin young woman stood as still as the flag that hung motionless in the summer air. Her head was bowed. The audience too was quiet. Suddenly she raised her head and paused, then ran at top speed. She leaped high into the air, clearing the high-jump bar. She jumped from the platform where she had landed, smiled widely, and raised her hands high above her head. The audience cheered and clapped wildly.

Conclusion: _____

_____

Detail: _____

_____

Detail: _____

_____

Apply **Write two sentences with details about a friend or member of your family. Then draw a conclusion about him or her from the details in the sentences. Write the conclusion in the space below.**

Sentence: _____

_____

Sentence: _____

_____

Conclusion: _____

Historical Fiction

 **Think** **Audience: Who** will read your historical fiction?

_____

Purpose: What is your reason for writing historical fiction?

_____

_____

_____

Prewriting **Use this graphic organizer to plan your historical fiction.**

In historical fiction, the	In my story, the
setting is a certain time and place in the past.	setting:
characters act how people of that time would have acted.	characters:
plot includes events or problems from that time.	plot:
details such as clothing, home, and transportation are true to the setting.	details:

Revising

Use this checklist to revise your historical fiction.

☐ Do your words clearly describe the time and place?

☐ Does your plot deal with problems or events from that time and place?

☐ Does the story sound like it could have really happened?

☐ Are the characters realistic and behave appropriate to the era?

Editing

Use this checklist to correct mistakes.

☐ Did you check all names and places for correct spelling?

☐ Did you check all punctuation and capitalization?

☐ Read aloud to catch grammar errors such as sentence fragments and run-on sentences.

☐ Make sure that each sentence and all proper nouns begin with a capital letter.

☐ Did you check your spelling, even if you used a spell-checking program?

Publishing

Use this checklist to get ready for publication.

☐ Check your story for any final errors.

☐ Write or type a neat final copy.

☐ Include illustrations or photographs. Present them neatly by pasting them onto a sheet of paper or by scanning and placing them in your electronic file.

☐ You can bind your story and keep a copy in your classroom for others to read.

☐ Compile all of your classmates' historical fiction pieces into a literary journal that can be placed in your classroom or the school library.

Greek Root *photo* and Greek Root *hydr*

Word List

1. *carbohydrate*

Focus

- Remember that the **Greek root photo** means "light," and the **Greek root hydr** means "water."

- Remember that Greek roots are a part of many words in the English language. Knowing these Greek roots can help you correctly define and spell words that are unfamiliar to you.

Practice   **Look up these spelling words in a dictionary, and write a short definition for each one.**

1. hydropower _____

2. hydrofoil _____

3. photogenic _____

4. hydraulic _____

5. photocopier _____

6. hydroplane _____

7. hydrogen _____

8. photosynthesis _____

11. *hydrometer*
12. *hydroplane*
13. *hydropower*
14. *hydrosphere*
15. *photocopier*
16. *photofinisher*
17. *photogenic*
18. *photosensitive*
19. *phototropic*
20. *telephoto*

Challenge Words

21. *hydrangea*

9. My mother planted a hydrangia in the garden. _____

10. The coach told the football team to hidrate with bottles of water.

_____

11. The journalist used to a telaphoto lens to snap the long-distance picture.

_____

12. The weather station had a barometer, thermometer, and hydromater.

_____

Match each word on the left to its definition on the right.

13. carbohydrate

a. Any of a group of organic compounds that includes sugars and starches, and gums and serves as a major energy source in the diet of animals.

14. hydrogen

b. To photograph well.

15. hydrometer

c. A colorless, odorless, flammable gas.

16. hydropower

d. A gauge that measures the specific gravity of a liquid.

17. photocopier

e. Energy generated from water.

18. photogenic

f. Pertaining to a photographic lens that allows a large image of a distant object.

19. telephoto

g. A machine that makes paper reproductions.

20. photosynthesis

h. The process through which plants convert carbon dioxide into oxygen through sunlight.

Appositives and Participial Phrases

Focus

- An **appositive** is a noun that is placed next to another noun to identify it or add information about it.

- An **appositive phrase** is a group of words that includes an appositive and words that describe the appositive. *(my best friend)*

- An appositive phrase can combine two sentences into one shorter sentence when one of the sentences provides additional information about something in the first sentence.

Example: Leeza sat talking to Kiyomi. Kiyomi was a fellow immigrant.

Leeza sat talking to Kiyomi, a fellow immigrant.

- A **participial phrase** functions as an adjective and includes a participle and other words that complete its meaning.

Example: *Walking home,* Kisha wondered what her mom would say.

Practice Circle the appositive phrase in each sentence.
Underline the noun it describes.

1. Papaw, my grandfather, takes me fishing every Saturday in the summer.

2. My cat, Tico, likes to chase bugs.

3. Our bus driver, Ms. Calhoun, is sick today.

4. White pizza, my favorite food, is on the menu today.

5. Little Bill, my neighbor, walks his dog early in the morning.

6. I just finished reading *Boggles*, my favorite book, for the fifth time.

7. The science fiction film, *Attack of the Spoiled Milk from Mars,* is on tonight!

8. The librarian, Mrs. Tate, said the book was reserved until January.

Read the following sentences, and underline the participial phrase in each.

9. Cluttered by magazines and newspapers, the table was not a very clean place to work.

10. Looking at us carefully, Claire said, "Are you sure you want to sit here?"

11. Reaching for her chair, she sat down slowly.

12. Sighing because I was tired of looking, I said, "Let's just clean it and sit down."

13. Shrugging their shoulders, the others went to look for paper towels.

14. Studying each shelf of videos, Dad finally settled on renting a movie with dinosaurs.

15. Listening to the lecture on Venus, I became interested in learning more about space.

Apply   **Write a short paragraph about your family. At least three of the sentences in your paragraph must include an appositive phrase.**

_____

_____

_____

_____

_____

_____

Inflectional Ending *-ing* and Contractions

 Focus
- The **inflectional ending *-ing*** is added to verbs to signify continuing action. Sometimes the final consonant of a word is doubled or the final vowel is dropped when adding this ending.
- A **contraction** is formed by combining two words, removing some of the letters, and connecting the words with an apostrophe.

Practice **Circle the correct form of the verb for each sentence.**

1. I could not believe she was still _____ the floors three hours later.

   mopped   mopping   mop

2. Sue did not want to _____ her lucky quarter for a gumball.

   tradIng   trade   traded

3. I was just _____!

   joke   joking   joked

4. He _____ the diagram so each part could be seen clearly.

   coloring   color   colored

5. Jack has been _____ every day this week.

   swimming   swam   swims

Circle the pair of words that make up each contraction.

6. didn't

   does not   did not   will not

7. should've

   could have   should not   should have

8. I'll

    I would   I did   I will

9. you'd

    you have   you would   you can

10. it's

    it does   it is   it should

Apply   **Add the inflectional ending *-ing* to the words below, and write the new word on the line. Be careful of spelling changes.**

11. shop _____

12. bring _____

13. ice _____

14. follow _____

15. dry _____

16. bathe _____

Use the words below to form contractions. Write the contractions on the lines provided.

17. she will _____

18. they have _____

19. will not _____

20. I have _____

Selection Vocabulary

Focus

expedition (ek' spə dish' ən) *n.* a group of people making a journey (page 306)

reliable (ri lī' ə bəl) *adj.* able to be depended on and trusted (page 306)

irresistibly (īr' i zīs' tə blē) *adv.* enticing; tempting to possess (page 307)

boasts (bōsts) *v.* form of **boast:** to talk too much or with too much pride about oneself; to brag (page 308)

flanked (flangkt) *v.* past tense of **flank:** to be at the side of (page 308)

clichés (klē shāz') *n.* plural of **cliché:** an overused expression or idea (page 309)

distill (di stil') *v.* to condense; to make simpler (page 309)

lure (lŏŏr) *v.* to attract strongly (page 310)

virtual (vûr' chü əl) *adj.* essence or effect, but not fact or real (page 311)

descendants (di send' ənts) *n.* plural of **descendant:** a person, animal, or plant whose descent can be traced to a particular individual or group (page 313)

beacon (bē' kən) *n.* a light or other signal that warns or guides ships or aircraft (page 313)

magnitude (mag' ni tüd') *n.* greatness of size (page 315)

Practice Write the vocabulary word next to the group of words that have a similar meaning.

1. trustworthy; solid; unfailing _____

2. attract; entice; tempt _____

3. amount; hugeness; largeness _____

4. guide; lighthouse; light _____

5. brags; flaunts; shows off _____

6. caravan; team; voyagers _____

7. almost; essentially; artificial _____

8. water down; condense; reduce _____

9. Try to make your writing original by avoiding (descendants / clichés) and other overused phrases.

10. Our (expedition / clichés) included six skilled climbers and a guide.

11. They could see the (boasts / beacon) onshore, so they knew they were getting close.

12. If you are going to start a business, you need to find a (reliable / virtual) partner who will not let you down.

13. The park (flanked / boasts) his neighborhood, so it was a convenient place to go jogging.

14. The (lure / magnitude) of the roller coaster was so intimidating that I was too nervous to ride it.

15. The teacher needed to (expedition / distill) the long, complicated text so the students could understand it.

16. Make sure you pack your food away so you don't (lure / distill) any bears to the campsite.

Write a brief paragraph using several of the vocabulary words from this lesson.

_____

_____

_____

_____

_____

_____

_____

Inflectional Ending *-ing*, Latin Root *prim*, and Contractions

Focus

- Remember that the **inflectional ending -*ing*** shows that something is happening now.
- For words ending in *e*, drop the *e* before adding *-ing*, as in (*practice* or *practicing*.)
- For words ending in short vowel plus *p*, short vowel plus *t*, or short vowel plus *m*, double the final consonant before adding *-ing*, (as in *nap, napping; hit, hitting*.)
- Remember that the **Latin root *prim*** means "first."
- Remember that **contractions** are new words formed from one or more individual words.

Practice

Add the inflectional ending *-ing* to the words below to create new ones.

1. dial _____

2. admire _____

3. accept _____

4. cook _____

Add the Latin root *prim* to the following endings.

5. *-itive* _____

6. *-al* _____

7. *-ary* _____

Combine the following words into contractions.

8. have, not _____

9. they, are _____

10. you, would _____

Word List

1. accepting
2. admiring
3. backpacking
4. bouncing
5. brainstorming
6. centering
7. challenging
8. chirping
9. cooking
10. dialing
11. doesn't
12. endangering
13. haven't
14. let's
15. planting
16. primary
17. primitive
18. they're
19. we've
20. you'd

Challenge Words

21. downloading
22. primer
23. primordial

Write five sentences that use contractions.

11. _____

_____

12. _____

_____

13. _____

_____

14. _____

_____

15. _____

_____

Apply The National Weather Service has just announced that a tornado watch is in effect for your school. Write a paragraph that describes how you feel. What safety measures should your school take? In your paragraph, include three uses of the inflectional ending *-ing,* one word that uses the Latin root *prim,* and at least two contractions.

_____

_____

_____

_____

_____

_____

_____

_____

Comparatives and Superlatives

Focus

- A **comparative adjective** compares two things. Comparative adjectives add *-er* to most one-syllable adjectives. Use *more* in front of most adjectives that have two or more syllables, but do not add *-er* to the end of the adjective.

- A **comparative adverb** compares two actions. To form comparative adverbs, add *-er* to most one-syllable adverbs and use *more* with most adverbs that have two or more syllables.

- A **superlative adjective** compares three or more things. Superlative forms of most one-syllable adjectives end in *-est*. Use the word *most* with most adjectives that have two or more syllables.

- A **superlative adverb** compares three or more actions. To make superlative adverbs, add *-est* to most one-syllable adverbs. Use the word *most* with most adverbs that have two or more syllables.

Practice **Circle the correct comparative adverb in each of the following sentences.**

1. Gracie played (quietlier/more quietly) than her sister.

2. I thought Carrin handled the news (more well/better) than I did.

3. The diver performed (more bad/worse) than her opponent.

4. Pierre completed his quiz (more confidently/confidentlier) than me.

5. Nina threw the discus (more far/farther) than she did at the last meet.

6. My little brother colors (precisely/more precisely) than he used to do.

7. I mow the lawn (better/more well) now than I did on my first try.

8. Jean-Luc was the (fastest/most fast) to say, "Make it so."

Write the comparative form of the boldfaced adjectives on the line provided.

9. **great** _____

10. **quick** _____

11. **creative** _____

12. **pretty** _____

13. **optimistic** _____

14. **hopeful** _____

15. **costly** _____

16. **hot** _____

17. **poor** _____

18. **simple** _____

 **Apply** **Cross out the incorrect form of each superlative adjective and adverb in the following paragraph, and write the correct form above it.**

Animals are the interestingest and sometimes the most strangest living things on Earth. Did you know that the Goliath beetle, weighing 3.5 ounces, is the most heaviest insect in the world? The sailfish, at 68 miles per hour, swims quickliest of all fish. The Australian sea wasp has the more painfulest sting of all animals. The two-toed sloth moves slowlier than any other mammal and spends most of its life in trees. Howler monkeys make the louder sounds of all primates. Their voices can be heard up to three miles away.

Vocabulary Word Web Resources

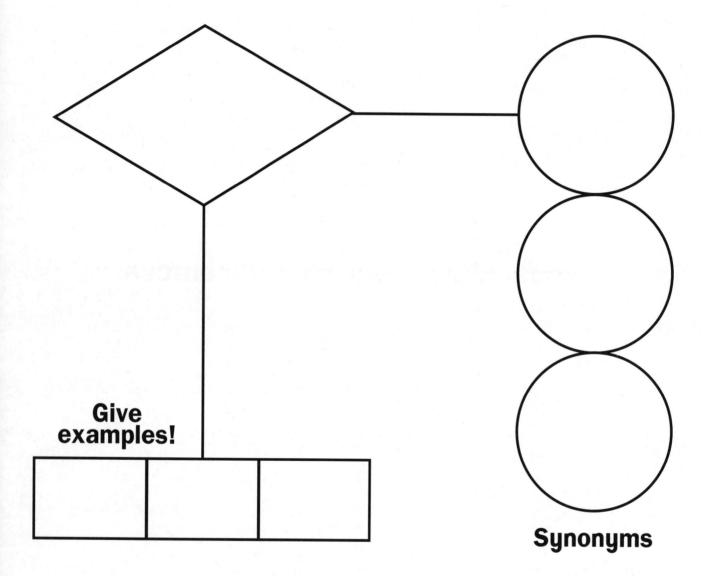

Give examples!

Synonyms

Examples

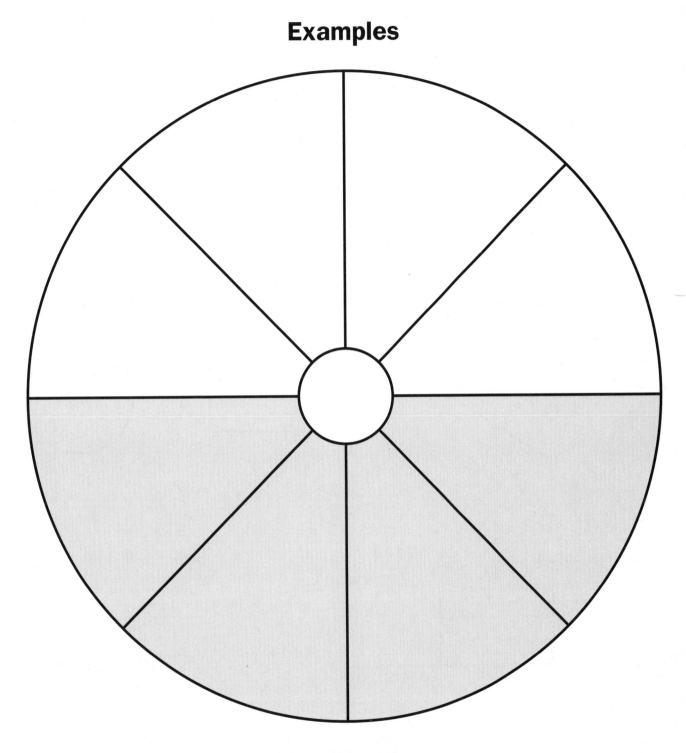

Not Examples

Specific   **General**

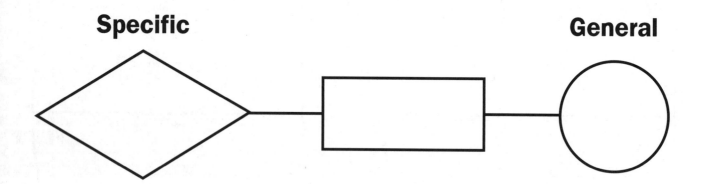

```
┌─────────────────────────┐              ┌─────────────────────────┐
│                         │              │                         │
│  ───────────────────    │     ╭───╮    │  ───────────────────    │
│                         │     │ Y │    │                         │
│  ───────────────────    │     ╰───╯    │  ───────────────────    │
│                         │              │                         │
│  ───────────────────    │     ╭───╮    │  ───────────────────    │
│                         │     │ N │    │                         │
│  ───────────────────    │     ╰───╯    │  ───────────────────    │
│                         │              │                         │
└─────────────────────────┘              └─────────────────────────┘
```

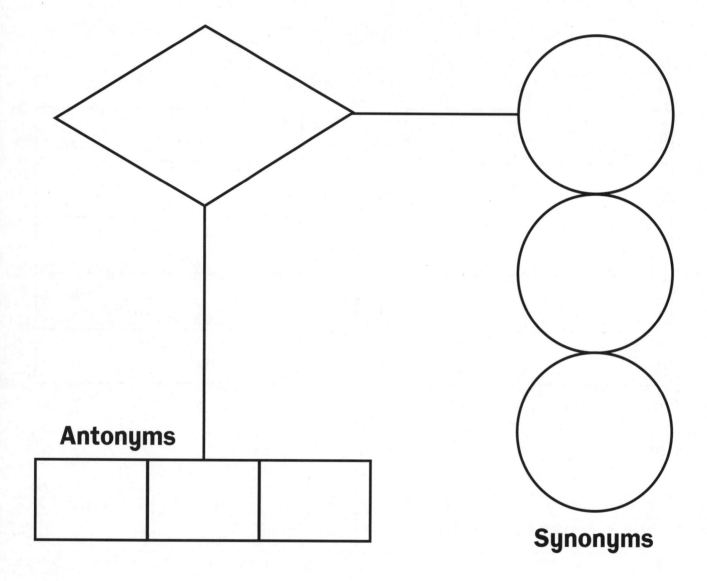

Antonyms

Synonyms

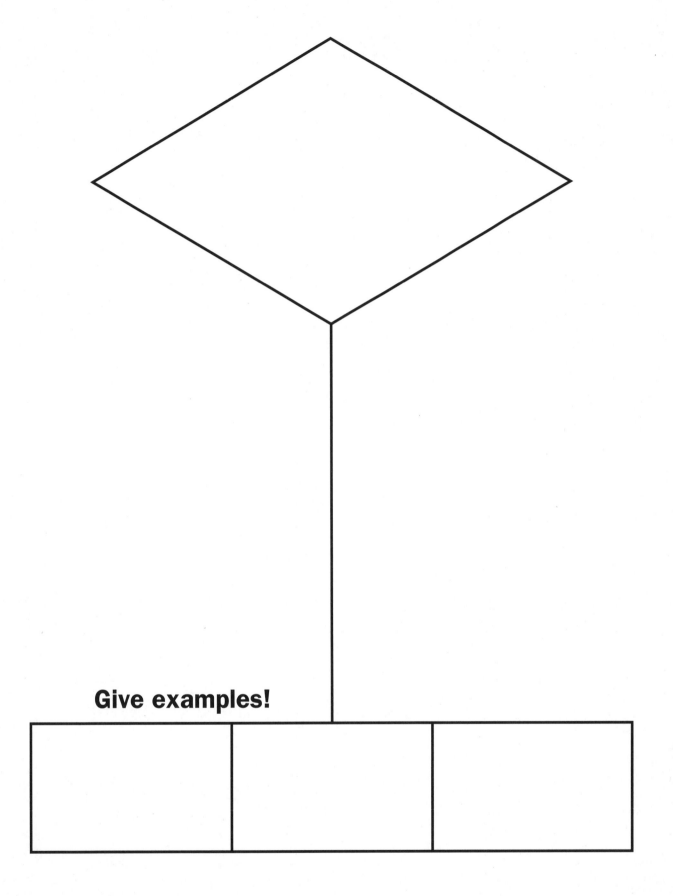

Give examples!